CW00656211

# THE
# DAD
# BOOK

An Hachette UK Company
www.hachette.co.uk

Summersdale Publishers Ltd
Part of Octopus Publishing Group Limited
Carmelite House
50 Victoria Embankment
LONDON
EC4Y 0DZ
UK

www.summersdale.com

Printed and bound in Poland

ISBN: 978-1-80007-099-8

Substantial discounts on bulk quantities of Summersdale books are available to corporations, professional associations and other organizations. For details contact general enquiries: telephone: +44 (0) 1243 771107 or email: enquiries@summersdale.com.

# THE DAD BOOK

## An Awesome Collection of
### QUIZZES, PUZZLES, LIFE HACKS, TRIVIA, JOKES AND MORE!

## Dan Bridges

summersdale

# INTRODUCTION

Welcome, dads!

Being a dad is rewarding, but it can be hard work. Oh boy, can it be hard work! Whether you're coaching sports teams, arranging school runs or simply being there to lend a helping hand, as a dad you have plenty of responsibilities to fit into your busy life.

So what better way to relax than with a book devoted entirely to dads? Prepare to be challenged and amazed in equal measure with this handy volume.

You have in your hands a book that will entertain you for hours. It's packed with fiendish puzzles that'll test your mental ability, ingenious hacks to make your life easier, jaw-dropping trivia and fantastic quizzes. Oh, and there are plenty of "dad jokes" that are sure to be a hit in your local bar – or you can use them on your children to produce the desired "oh, dad" groan!

*The Dad Book* is written with the modern father in mind. If it serves as a cerebral sanctuary or as an informative manual – or even as a humorous eye-opener – it will have done its job.

So, settle down in your favourite armchair, crack open a beer and while away a few pleasurable hours in the company of *The Dad Book*.

# ANAGRAM

Dads can be notoriously technophobic, so here's an anagram to help you overcome your technology fears. The top row of a standard keyboard/typewriter consists of the following ten letters:

# QWERTYUIOP

Can you find a ten-letter word? You can use any letter more than once and omit as many as you want.

# WE ASKED 100 PEOPLE

The questions below were asked to 100 people. Can you guess the top three answers to each one?

1. **Name a type of "keeper".**

2. **Name someone you might be nervous to meet for the first time.**

3. **Name a way of travelling long distances without an engine.**

4. **Name a flower you see in spring.**

5. **Name a famous figure who is green.**

# WORD SEARCH

As a dad, trekking in the great outdoors with your children can be one of life's simple pleasures. Find all the words below to see if you're the adventurer you claim to be!

**Lake**

**Woodland**

**Forest**

**Flask**

**Thermal socks**

**Moors**

**Map**

**Compass**

**Rucksack**

**Walking stick (sorry, young dads!)**

```
J  H  A  V  C  K  R  W  S  X  G  I  K  M  W
G  H  Y  H  S  F  D  A  A  R  T  Y  H  B  A
F  D  A  A  S  A  Z  X  C  V  B  L  Y  H  L
R  P  L  S  H  I  M  O  U  N  T  A  I  N  K
W  F  T  D  C  D  F  H  B  N  J  K  Y  G  I
J  O  L  A  K  A  L  M  N  B  H  E  F  C  N
J  U  O  T  R  U  C  K  S  A  C  K  J  N  G
M  K  O  D  J  H  Y  G  F  R  E  Y  A  N  S
Z  K  F  R  L  S  P  L  M  N  M  Y  F  C  T
E  S  G  J  O  A  M  B  G  H  Y  O  C  X  I
K  U  F  R  M  C  N  B  H  J  I  J  O  M  C
H  G  H  V  C  X  S  D  R  D  F  Y  H  R  K
T  H  E  R  M  A  L  S  O  C  K  S  C  H  S
M  B  F  Y  A  B  C  I  F  O  R  E  S  T  R
G  C  O  M  P  A  S  S  G  Y  A  F  T  D  P
```

# DAD JOKES

KNOCK, KNOCK.
WHO'S THERE?
THE INTERRUPTING COW.
THE INTERUP—
MOOOO!

---

KNOCK, KNOCK.
WHO'S THERE?
TANK
TANK WHO?
YOU'RE VERY WELCOME!

# CRYPTICALLY
# CLUED-UP

All the answers to these cryptic clues have a link – but what's the connection?

1. **WARNING! Plot development revealed (esp. in films)**

2. **Punctuation mark similar to a hyphen**

3. **Type of bridge (e.g. Golden Gate)**

4. **Employees are given this when fired (expression)**

5. **Long muscular proboscis**

# TRIVIA ABOUT TRIVIA

For decades, *Guinness World Records* (formerly *The Guinness Book of Records*) has been the authority on facts, figures and general trivia – verified by professionals across the globe.

But did you know that the idea for the book arose in the early 1950s and that the concept came down to a game bird? Yep, while on a shooting party in County Wexford, the managing director of the Guinness brewery, Sir Hugh Beaver, argued with his shooting colleagues as to the identity of the fastest game bird in Europe. No reference book came up with the answer. Surely there was a need for a book containing definitive details of record-breakers?

After copious amounts of research, work began on the first draft of the book – which took nearly fourteen 90-hour weeks. As the book's popularity increased, it became a regular bestseller, as well as the volume most stolen from public libraries.

And the book has the fastest European game bird to thank for its success.

(It's the golden plover, in case you were wondering!)

# DAD JOKES

*I ONCE THOUGHT I WAS
A 1980s POP SINGER.
IN FACT, I WAS ADAM ANT!*

---

*HOW DOES A COWBOY
ROUND UP 19 COWS?
HE JUST CALLS IT 20 COWS.*

---

*TO WHOEVER STOLE
MY ANTIDEPRESSANTS:
I HOPE YOU'RE HAPPY.*

# AVOIDING BLUNT RAZORS

Every dad has undoubtedly been in this situation: there's an important evening coming up and you've realized that the few days' stubble needs to be shaved off to produce gloriously smooth skin. But, disaster! Your razor is looking a little rusty and you don't have enough time to go to the nearest convenience shop.

What to do? Simply run your razor along denim jeans, in the opposite direction to the one you'd use if you were shaving, approximately 15 times. Sorted – you should now have, er… razor-sharp blades! Word to the wise: you should probably take the jeans off and rest them on a solid base! You're a grown man, so you shouldn't need reminding to be careful of newly sharpened blades before you do this!

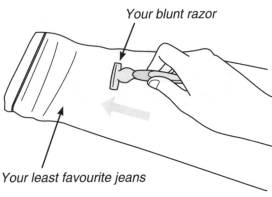

*Your blunt razor*

*Your least favourite jeans*

# THE NAME'S BOND...
# JAMES BOND

Ever dreamed of being the ultimate on-screen spy? Of course you have – you're a dad! Test your knowledge of 007 with this Bond-related quiz. Award yourself a licence to kill if you do well... But it's time to retire your Aston Martin to the garage if you come up short!

1. Which was Pierce Brosnan's first Bond film?

2. How many Bond film titles consist of just one word?

3. Who is the main villain in *Thunderball*?

4. Which film features Bond famously skiing off a cliff before opening up his Union Jack parachute?

5. Who plays Mary Goodnight in *The Man with the Golden Gun*?

6. Bond challenges Auric Goldfinger to which sport?

7. Which Bond film features May Day?

8. What does the "R" stand for in the acronym SPECTRE?

# GET GREAT PECS THE MORE YOU BREW

How many cups of coffee or tea do you drink per day? Three, four? And what do you do while waiting for the kettle to boil? Probably nothing, right? Well, think again, dads!

Put your water-boiling waiting time to excellent use by performing press-ups on the edge of your kitchen counter. On average, 40 press-ups can be performed every time the kettle is activated. That's about 120 press-ups per day as you wait, and you probably won't even know you're doing them. In about a month – or after about a hundred brews – you should have noticeably toned pecs. Beats going to the gym!

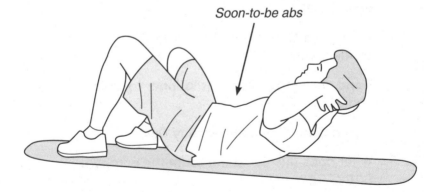

*Soon-to-be abs*

# ANAGRAMS

Think you know your female singers? Unravel the five anagrams below to find out!

1. SHUT BEAK

2. A DAFT SILLINESS

3. THE CHORAL CRUTCH

4. MATE IS LOONY

5. HERE IS SHINY CD

# WORD SEARCH

Dads are special, but we're all mammals at heart (some more than others!). Spot all these mammals in the grid to achieve maximum intelligence!

**Orangutan**

**Fennec fox**

**Hyena**

**Jackal**

**Dolphin**

**Porcupine**

**Weasel**

**Leopard**

**Coyote**

**Chipmunk**

| | | | | | | | | | | | | | | |
|---|---|---|---|---|---|---|---|---|---|---|---|---|---|---|
| A | N | V | G | H | Y | R | D | X | Z | K | O | L | H | A |
| F | R | F | E | N | N | E | C | F | O | X | K | E | N | C |
| G | F | T | W | D | C | X | D | Y | J | A | N | O | G | H |
| H | C | P | G | E | E | Q | S | Z | V | K | M | P | F | I |
| H | Y | O | J | G | A | C | B | K | P | I | Y | A | U | P |
| R | E | R | Y | Z | X | S | H | I | K | A | F | R | K | M |
| H | F | C | O | O | T | D | E | S | J | B | N | D | F | U |
| Y | D | U | A | D | T | E | G | L | H | A | V | C | F | N |
| E | Y | P | G | C | C | E | A | A | T | J | C | N | H | K |
| N | K | I | A | U | H | G | D | U | J | K | M | K | A | F |
| A | S | N | Y | A | J | B | G | C | G | U | I | P | A | A |
| H | A | E | G | E | V | N | D | F | V | T | D | D | S | L |
| F | J | B | V | A | A | B | V | F | G | C | A | I | J | N |
| J | K | M | N | R | Y | T | D | O | L | P | H | I | N | C |
| C | T | R | O | D | F | J | O | K | H | G | Y | G | F | R |

# CROSSWORD

Late-night food choices are a man's prerogative. See how many of these finger-lickin' dishes you can find.

1. **Want scraps with that? (4, 3, 5)**

2. **Italian staple made in a US state? (8, 5)**

3. **Nutty Chinese dish with crustaceans – fit for royalty? (4, 5, 5)**

4. **No ordinary egg-based dish (7, 8)**

5. **Mexican shells filled with fowl (7, 5)**

6. **Meaty low-heat curry (4, 5)**

7. **Dairy food on a quarter-pounder (12)**

8. **Something spicy for the weekend (8)**

# WORD SEARCH

"You disrespect this word search, you disrespect the family!" Find these well-known gangster and crime films in the grid below.

**Scarface**

**Goodfellas**

**The Godfather**

**Casino**

**Carlito's Way**

**The Departed**

**Get Carter**

**Legend**

**Heat**

**The Irishman**

```
K  L  B  C  R  D  O  J  G  D  A  T  H  T  U
I  G  E  T  C  A  R  T  E  R  C  K  A  H  A
C  B  V  G  U  I  H  G  C  S  X  E  O  E  B
A  F  T  F  E  D  S  H  J  N  H  G  Y  D  J
R  F  S  V  N  N  U  R  D  G  N  M  L  E  J
I  X  R  G  H  B  D  V  X  J  L  M  H  P  G
I  S  A  I  J  H  F  N  O  C  T  V  C  A  O
T  C  T  H  E  G  O  D  F  A  T  H  E  R  O
O  F  T  G  V  G  A  M  L  S  V  C  F  T  D
S  C  A  R  F  A  C  E  K  I  G  F  R  E  F
W  C  B  N  H  C  D  R  Y  N  M  L  J  D  E
A  R  Y  B  C  X  H  I  M  O  I  A  P  K  L
Y  D  A  V  C  D  H  A  B  F  H  M  K  L  L
N  B  V  C  F  T  T  U  H  F  T  D  S  E  A
T  H  E  I  R  I  S  H  M  A  N  A  P  K  S
```

# ?

# I'M AFRAID
# I DON'T KNOW
# WHAT YOU MEAN!

Dads – don't be scared! Which is the correct meaning for each phobia?

**1) PERISTEROPHOBIA**

a) **Fear of folded objects**

b) **Fear of pigeons**

c) **Fear of cattle grids**

**2) MAGEIROCOPHOBIA**

a) **Fear of cleaning**

b) **Fear of cooking**

c) **Fear of vacuuming**

**3) ALEMERCIALICEPTIOPHOBIA**

a) **Fear of beer not being as it is in commercials**

b) **Fear of buying a round of drinks**

c) **Fear of spilling an alcoholic beverage over one's spouse**

# DAD JOKES

JOKES ABOUT WHITE SUGAR ARE RARE.
BUT JOKES ABOUT BROWN SUGAR...
DEMERARA.

---

WHAT DO YOU CALL A YOUNG SHEEP
IN SWIMWEAR DRIVING A FAST CAR?
A LAMB BIKINI.

---

MY VACUUM CLEANER WAS ILL,
BUT IT'S NOW RECOVERING.
YOU COULD SAY IT'S PICKING UP NICELY.

# EARLY BAND NAMES

Dads like to sing in front of mirrors and play air guitar whenever possible – provided no one's looking! Maybe you have dreams (or delusions!) of making it to the big stage in a band? Everyone started somewhere! Take a look at these famous musical acts, because they all certainly started somewhere… and their names developed over time. Give it some time and you, too, could be ditching your original name for a more marketable one!

Blur – Seymour

Beach Boys – Carl and the Passions

Led Zeppelin – The New Yardbirds

Lynyrd Skynyrd – My Backyard

Righteous Brothers – Paramours

The Beatles – Johnny and the Moondogs

The Bangles – The Bangs

Depeche Mode – Composition of Sound

Black Sabbath – The Polka Tulk Blues Band

Blondie – Angel and the Snake

Steppenwolf – The Sparrows

# DINGBAT

Dads often use lateral thinking in everyday life, but can you work out this devilish dingbat?

# TIT♂♂♂ANIC

# HOW TO UN–MAT CURLY HAIR

Oh, to have a mop of luscious curly hair! But, for some dads, this blessing is also a curse – especially when it comes to combing those springy locks.

Don't despair! The trick to detangling wavy or twisted curls is to apply hair wax on clean hair (after a shower, for instance), dry sparingly with a towel and then REPEAT the whole process. OK, so it's double the work, but you'll also be ultra clean, and your hair will be so much easier to comb or brush the second time around. Then it's just a case of choosing your hairstyle!

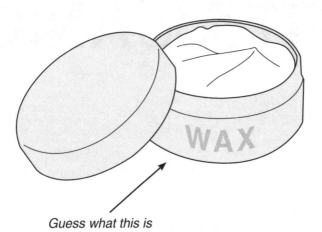

*Guess what this is*

# DAD JOKES

I'VE JUST BOUGHT AN ABBA TOILET.
WHAT A LOO!

---

I ONCE SAT IN A PUB FOR
FIVE HOURS, WRAPPING
BANDAGES AROUND MY BEER.
THE BARMAN GOT ANGRY AND
YELLED, "GET OUT — YOU'VE BEEN
NURSING THAT PINT FOR AGES!"

---

WHERE DO YOU LEARN TO
MAKE A BANANA SPLIT?
SUNDAE SCHOOL.

# WORD LADDER

Don't be a dope! Change one letter at a time to get to a four-letter word enjoyed by dads all across the land.

**DOPE**

**PINT**

# FIZZY TRIVIA

Next time you pop a can of Fanta, think about the beginnings of this famous fizzy drink.

When Coca-Cola was embargoed in 1940s Nazi Germany, the head of the country's branch of the company needed to come up with an alternative drink. The name Fanta was chosen when employees were asked to "use their imagination" ("*Fantasie*" in German), and an eager salesman responded with: "Fanta!"

In 1943, approximately three million cases of Fanta were sold – but many of these were not drunk. Instead, they were used as sweeteners to add to soups and stews, since wartime sugar was heavily rationed.

Who would have thought that one of the most widely sold soft drinks in history arose because of a trade embargo that affected the availability of Coca-Cola ingredients?

Today, Fanta is enjoyed throughout the world by hundreds of millions of thirsty drinkers – no doubt unaware of its wartime origins.

# WORD SEARCH

Dads can be romantic souls. No, they can, really! Spot all the titles of love songs to get you in the mood!

**"My Girl"**

**"Unchained Melody"**

**"Hello"**

**"Cherish"**

**"Eternal Flame"**

**"Pray"**

**"The Best"**

**"Kiss from a Rose"**

**"Your Song"**

**"Heartbeat"**

```
A K I S S F R O M A R O S E D
E S W A J N B G H I E L P J H
V A D S A E T B V C T Y J N V
U N C H A I N E D M E L O D Y
G A H H B G Y H M K R A O Y B
H H Y G E T A D X S N V B O A
Y M J M K R L L I K A P L U H
G Y F R D S I C V B L M I R N
A G Y U J U Y S A O F K J S T
G I A H G F T T H A L C F O H
P R A Y N J J G Y J A K L N E
H L B U G F D R T Y M L V G B
G T D S E M N B V H E K P L E
K H G H Y A F F T H F A T A S
H G A H E A R T B E A T L L T
```

# MISSING LETTER

Dads often know a lot about rugby, so why not prove just *how much* you know with this puzzle? Each of the following words is missing a letter; put all of them into the grid below to reveal the surname of a former rugby union player.

**1** TWI_E

**2** P_PER

**3** RU_BLE

**4** EM_LOY

**5** ANG_L

**6** DO_ES

**7** SM_LL

| 1 | 2 | 3 | 4 | 5 | 6 | 7 |
|---|---|---|---|---|---|---|
|   |   |   |   |   |   |   |

# PREMIER LEAGUE

Even the top footballers need a helping hand. The following ten players have all helped teammates to score goals, either in the form of a corner or a killer pass. Rank them in order of number of assists from most to least – just don't score an own goal!

___ **David Beckham**

___ **Ryan Giggs**

___ **Steven Gerrard**

___ **Frank Lampard**

___ **Wayne Rooney**

___ **Teddy Sheringham**

___ **David Silva**

___ **Thierry Henry**

___ **Cesc Fàbregas**

___ **Dennis Bergkamp**

# FOUR BY FOUR

Super-brainy dads should have no problem with this nifty crossword – I hope!

| 1 | 2 | 3 | 4 |
|---|---|---|---|
| 5 |   |   |   |
| 6 |   |   |   |
| 7 |   |   |   |

**ACROSS**

**1** 2-2 in football?

**5** Alleviate

**6** Dr – Austin Powers' nemesis

**7** Peruse

**DOWN**

**1** Expensive animal?

**2** Rant in a nightclub?

**3** Continent

**4** Fuse (esp. metals)

# CLEAN WHITE SHOELACES

Your trainers might be in optimum condition, but what about your laces? It's all too easy for these ties to acquire the pesky brown colour of General Grime. If you want to put your best foot forward on the tennis or squash court, you'd better take control of the situation – and fast!

Help is at hand! Speaking of hands, first put on a pair of rubber gloves. Simply fill a bowl with soda water, add to it approximately 1 tsp of peroxide and a tablespoon of baking soda, and then give it a brisk whisk. Whip out your shoelaces and submerge them in the bubbly concoction for five minutes. What do we have here? Gleaming white shoelaces that even Roger Federer would be proud of.

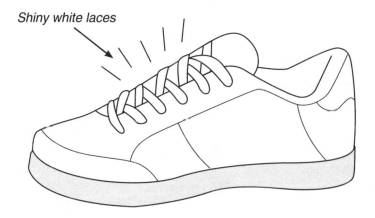

*Shiny white laces*

# WORD SEARCH

What's better than putting your feet up for an afternoon of watching snooker? Find these surnames of famous snooker players to achieve a maximum break.

**Murphy**

**Davis**

**Hendry**

**Reardon**

**O'Sullivan**

**Selby**

**Trump**

**Williams**

**Higgins**

**Bingham**

```
P  T  N  B  H  H  G  C  F  D  S  Z  X  T  W
H  K  R  M  N  B  I  N  G  H  A  M  T  G  I
U  O  K  U  N  H  J  K  O  L  P  L  K  H  L
M  Y  G  G  M  C  X  A  F  T  H  U  K  A  L
U  L  J  H  G  P  G  F  A  D  E  T  T  G  I
R  M  B  G  T  Y  H  K  K  P  L  L  J  V  A
P  F  G  T  H  J  I  J  J  A  V  C  F  G  M
H  J  K  K  L  S  V  D  H  I  G  G  I  N  S
Y  C  A  G  F  D  E  X  C  N  H  T  Y  J  O
K  M  B  O  S  U  L  L  I  V  A  N  A  M  H
G  F  G  I  H  J  O  L  B  N  B  A  G  Y  G
J  N  V  U  K  M  N  V  G  Y  O  M  J  G  A
O  A  A  K  K  N  G  T  R  S  T  J  P  L  M
D  G  F  H  E  N  D  R  Y  R  G  U  J  M  A
K  M  U  U  G  F  R  E  A  R  D  O  N  V  G
```

# DAD JOKES

AN ORANGE AND A LEMON
WALK INTO A BAR.
THE LEMON SAYS, "YOUR ROUND."

---

THE INVENTOR OF THE
JUG DIED RECENTLY.
TRIBUTES HAVE BEEN POURING IN...

---

A WIFE LEFT HER HUSBAND
BECAUSE HE WAS GOING BALD.
HE WASN'T BOTHERED — ACCORDING
TO HIM, "IT'S HAIR LOSS!"

# LINKWORD

Find the missing link: the first and second word of each set go together, as do the second and third. Dads – come on, you've got this nailed!

**1** BACK _ _ _ _ _ _ BREAKING

**2** FIRE _ _ _ _ BEARING

**3** OVER _ _ _ _ UP

**4** RED _ _ _ HEAVY

**5** EYE _ _ _ _ POINT

# WORD SEARCH

Raise your glass to the wonderful world of beer by seeking out the words below.

**Hops**

**Barley**

**Pint**

**Barrel**

**Firkin**

**Yeast**

**Brewery**

**Ale**

**Stout**

**Lager**

| A | K | H | V | G | A | C | B | A | R | L | E | Y | X | G |
|---|---|---|---|---|---|---|---|---|---|---|---|---|---|---|
| I | Y | A | A | O | S | J | G | V | C | F | T | E | D | B |
| N | M | L | H | U | G | T | X | X | E | G | B | A | H | K |
| M | L | E | L | J | H | N | O | A | G | Y | T | S | R | D |
| P | L | M | N | G | Y | T | F | U | X | D | S | T | I | J |
| L | A | J | J | U | A | G | F | T | T | D | A | U | H | N |
| A | K | M | J | A | H | C | D | F | R | G | J | A | O | A |
| G | I | C | Y | T | A | N | B | V | F | F | G | H | U | J |
| E | M | M | N | H | L | V | G | H | J | I | L | P | L | K |
| R | Y | H | Y | E | F | B | R | E | W | E | R | Y | E | D |
| F | N | B | R | G | F | R | D | U | I | O | L | K | J | H |
| Y | H | R | F | R | D | A | D | D | G | V | C | D | I | H |
| J | A | K | U | T | H | O | P | S | E | F | G | H | N | N |
| B | F | G | Y | H | K | H | H | P | I | N | T | N | B | D |
| S | E | D | G | H | U | K | L | O | I | U | H | F | A | Z |

# FAMOUS INSOMNIACS

Do you ever get to 9 p.m. and fancy putting your feet up for a snooze? Of course you do – you're a dad. But think about those who would like to do just that, only to find they simply can't doze off. Here are a trio of well-known people who suffered from insomnia.

1. **Mark Twain** – a notable insomniac, the famous author once stayed over at a friend's house and hurled a pillow at the bedroom window in frustration at his sleepless state. He heard a crash and, assuming his irritable assault had let in some fresh air, he instantly fell asleep. In the morning, however, he discovered he had thrown the pillow at a glass bookcase.

2. **Theodore Roosevelt** – the US president's sure-fire insomnia cure was a shot of cognac in a glass of milk.

3. **Chuck Palahniuk** – the US author best known for 1996's *Fight Club* once found himself stranded in Reno, Nevada, penniless, exhausted due to insomnia and with nowhere to stay. His wanderings around all-night casinos and restaurants inspired his character simply called The Narrator, who suffers from chronic insomnia. The cult novel was made into a 1999 film starring Edward Norton as the protagonist.

**!**

# WOULD YOU BELIEVE IT?

In May 1997, thieves climbed a fence at the home of Bob Hodgson. They broke open two locks and stole valuable "merchandise". It was the perfect robbery, except for one slight oversight. What was it?

**1 Bob Hodgson was the most senior lawyer in his town and he had all the latest home security equipment. The thieves were identified on the same night of the crime and immediately apprehended.**

**2 The "merchandise" was a solid gold statue of Zeus. Though alluring, it proved too heavy for the forklift truck, which the thieves had also stolen on the same day to manoeuvre the golden Greek god from Mr Hodgson's garden.**

**3 The stolen "merchandise" was numerous homing pigeons – all but eight flew back to Mr Hodgson.**

# DAPPER ANAGRAMS

Here is a selection of anagrams that relate to men's clothing. How fashionable!

1. **TARVAC**

2. **ZEBRAL**

3. **REMBOB TAKJEC**

4. **SINPIPRET UTIS**

5. **LAFT PAC**

# VOWEL CAN YOU WORK THESE OUT?

Here are the names of some famous golfers – but with their vowels deleted. Will you score a hole-in-one or a double bogey?

1. **TGR WDS**

2. **RN LS**

3. **DSTN JHNSN**

4. **JRDN SPTH**

5. **FRNCSC MLNR**

6. **HNRK STNSN**

7. **BRKS KPK**

8. **BRYSN DCHMB**

9. **N PLTR**

# DAD JOKES

A MAN TOLD HIS THERAPIST
HE COULDN'T GET THE GREASE
SOUNDTRACK OUT OF HIS HEAD.
THE THERAPIST SAID, "TELL ME MORE!"

---

I ONCE KNEW A MUSIC FAN WHO
KEPT MAKING MOTOWN PUNS.
IT LASTED FOR ABOUT THREE
YEARS, FOUR TOPS...

---

A SKELETON WALKED INTO A BAR.
HE ORDERED A PINT OF
LAGER AND A MOP.

# IDENTITY (OR IDENTIFIABLE) CRISIS

Ever wondered which events in life are the most stressful? In the 1960s, Holmes and Rahe developed the Social Readjustment Rating Scale, which identifies the severity of major stressful events that individuals might experience in life. The scale, based on "life change units", has been altered over time to reflect changing values and cross-cultural differences.

And which are the top ten events that are likely to cause adults the most stress? Read on…

1. **Death of spouse**
2. **Divorce (see number nine in the list!)**
3. **Marital separation**
4. **Detention in jail**
5. **Death of close family member**
6. **Major personal injury or illness**
7. **Marriage**
8. **Being fired from work**
9. **Marital reconciliation**
10. **Retirement from work**

# THE GREAT BANANA SHOE–SHINE TRICK

Yep, you heard that correctly. This is not the title of a 1970s comedy B-movie. Oh no – it's an oh-so simple trick that can transform dreary leather shoes into a pair of gleaming footwear any dad would be proud to own.

You'll need three items: one pair of shoes, a clean cloth and a banana. Are you following?

Step one: Eat said banana (or simply throw away the fleshy bit and keep the skin).

Step two: Rub the banana skin – inner-side down – into your shoes until you see them start to shine.

Step three: Rub them down with the cloth and stand back in awe at how a humble, edible yellow thing can be *that* useful!

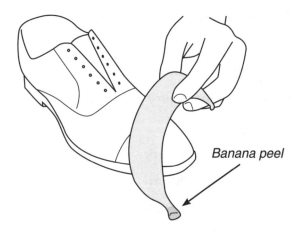

*Banana peel*

# WHAT ARE THE CHANCES?

Here's a little-known fact for all footie-mad dads – if you like the occasional flutter, this will suit you down to the ground. Read the incident below and work out the odds of it happening.

In January 2001, Worthing played Bromley in a Saturday football match. In the sixty-third minute, two players were sent off. All fairly ordinary up to here, right? However, both players – one from Bromley and one from Worthing – were called Danny Smith. After the match, players and fans speculated the odds of this happening. Bookmakers were contacted and it was estimated that the chances were…

a) 1,000–1

b) 10,000–1

c) 25,000–1

d) 50,000–1

# WHAT SCARES STEPHEN KING?

The "king" of modern horror has scared millions with his chilling imagination – both in print and on film. But what scares *him*? Take a look at the following five scenes from films that give Mr King the willies!

1. *Carrie* (1976). This was King's first published novel, which came out two years before the movie. The scene at the end of the flick when Sissy Spacek thrusts her hand out of the ground gets the author every time!

2. *Night of the Living Dead* (1968). A horror classic, George Romero's masterpiece turns King's legs to jelly – especially the scene in the cellar when the little girl stabs her mother to death with a garden trowel. (Well, that would scare anyone, right?)

3. *Psycho* (1960). Like millions of viewers, it's that shower scene that sends King scuttling behind the sofa!

4. *Wait Until Dark* (1967). King is always shocked when, toward the film's conclusion, Alan Arkin jumps out at Audrey Hepburn.

5. *I Bury the Living* (1958). The graveyard scene terrifies the horror master – watch it for yourself!

# MOVIE DINGBAT

Here's a short, but sweet, dingbat for all cinema-going dads.

## SHORT

# SHORT

↑

# LETTERBOX

Simply cross out the letters in the grid below that appear more than once. The remaining letters will then spell out a word, which is…?

| K | W | B | A | V |
|---|---|---|---|---|
| E | C | P | T | H |
| V | J | S | L | G |
| D | R | F | D | J |
| L | F | O | K | W |
| A | T | B | C | S |

# THIS REALLY IS GRATE

Picture the scene: you've promised your "better half" a romantic candlelit dinner with no interruptions. And you even pledged that all the prep and cooking will be conducted by your good self. How splendid.

But then – just as you're about to grate a carrot to complement a tasty salad – tragedy strikes: your grater turns out to be as sharp as a butter knife.

Best go to your trusty toolbox and whip out a bit of sandpaper (medium grade is preferable). Sand the "eyes" of the grate, going with the grain, and in no time you'll have blades sharp enough to slice through your carrots perfectly. Phew! Your salad is rescued.

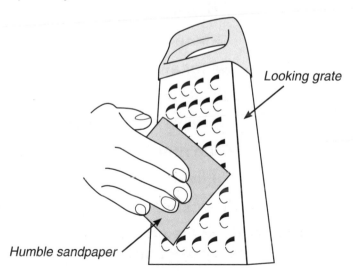

*Looking grate*

*Humble sandpaper*

# WORD SEARCH

If you're the man in the house, you'll be familiar with some of these "man tools". Get cracking and find them all!

**Claw hammer**

**Screwdriver**

**Sander**

**Dust mask**

**Nail gun**

**Chisel**

**Pliers**

**Planer**

**Bandsaw**

**Power drill**

**Square**

**Glue gun**

**Level**

**Putty knife**

**Tea break (come on – you'll definitely use that…)**

```
T N A I L G U N X V A M J H P
E T G H O K L A H B V G F A U
A C H H G F H U K W L A M D T
B H G T F D T G E F F H N U T
R I L J H S Y T F G A M S S Y
E S P A R U Q A G F U G C T K
A E F E T A D U A O S N R M N
K L I A H F F B A C D S E A I
G L J L S A N D E R A H W S F
P O W E R D R I L L E D D K E
N E K V H V C F D X C G R J O
K J H E Y Y C X A B B K I H G
Y Y P L A N E R L P L J V P S
B A N D S A W L N B H T E G D
F A X C L A W H A M M E R L Q
```

# ULTIMATE TASTE TEST

At some point, dads everywhere will have begged their children to just try one bite of a new food, only to be met with a look of youthful disdain. But when was the last time *you* ate something new and unfamiliar? Why not test your taste buds on some of the global delicacies below – some are a particularly acquired taste.

1. **Bat soup – apparently, the taste is similar to chicken!**

2. **Whole sheep's head – just hope it doesn't wink at you...**

3. **Casu marzu – pungent Sardinian cheese containing maggots. Lovely!**

4. **Live octopus – a delicacy in many places, including Japan and South Korea.**

5. **Boodog – a Mongolian speciality consisting of goat barbecued with heated stones inserted in the carcass.**

6. **"Stink heads" – Alaskan salmon heads, which have been buried for weeks and left to ferment.**

7. **Jellied moose nose – another Alaskan delicacy.**

8. **Bull penis – it's the penis of a bull.**

# DAD JOKES

A WIFE ASKED HER HUSBAND
IF HE'D SEEN THE DOG BOWL.
THE HUSBAND REPLIED THAT
HE DIDN'T EVEN KNOW THE
DOG PLAYED CRICKET.

---

A HUSBAND BOUGHT HIS WIFE
A FALSE LEG FOR CHRISTMAS.
IT WASN'T HER MAIN PRESENT —
JUST A STOCKING FILLER.

---

MY FRIEND SAYS HE ISN'T
ADDICTED TO BRAKE FLUID —
HE CAN STOP ANY TIME HE WANTS.

# TAKE FIVE

Here's one mini crossword: four clues and one red herring – which leaves three answers! Fit each answer twice into the grid below, once going across and once going down.

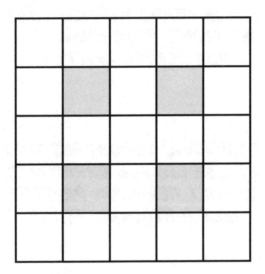

**CLUE 1: Formula One driver**
**CLUE 2: Snake**
**CLUE 3: European country**
**CLUE 4: The body's signal transmitter**

# PLASTIC-BAG HACK

Every home has one: a drawer where seemingly hundreds of plastic bags are kept. Fine. Except, when it's opened, the bags leap out like a domestic jack-in-the-box, causing alarm, frustration and a floor full of said plastic bags.

Go with this solution for floor-free bags. Simply acquire a small plastic container with a top (an ice-cream box will do) and cut a neat hole in the lid – roughly one centimetre (a square half-inch) is perfect. Then, put the first bag in the box, handles up. Take bag number two and thread the bottom through the handles of the first bag, and then push the first bag down into place in the container. Continue to do this until you've added all your bags, or the box is full, fit the lid onto the container and pull the handles of the last bag up through the hole. Every time you lift a handle, each bag comes out without fuss – in a fashion similar to heavy-duty cleaning wipes. Bingo!

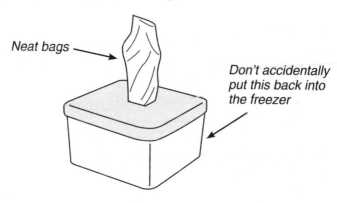

Neat bags

Don't accidentally put this back into the freezer

# CROSSWORD

Solve these fiendish clues to gain status of "Winning Dad".
Each answer is a sport.

1. Add "te" to make a deep-fried food (7)

2. Ice or field? (6)

3. Type of garden barrier (7)

4. Popular racquet sport – not fake (4, 6)

5. Racquet sport played at horse trials (9)

6. Chirpy insect (7)

7. Offence in soccer (8)

8. Played on a 9 x 5 feet (2.7 x 1.5 metres) surface (5, 6)

9. Minty sport (4)

10. Don't forget your parachute (9)

# THINK BEFORE YOU SPEAK!

Do you have the habit of blurting out the first thing that comes into your mind? That's dads, right? Here are eight fiendish questions where the correct answers are not as obvious as they seem. You must answer all of them in just *45 seconds*. Fair play to you if score a perfect eight!

1. **What colour are the breasts of blue tits?**

2. **What type of creature was Buffalo Bill famous for killing?**

3. **Panama hats originated from which country?**

4. **What type of animal inspired the creation of Bugs Bunny?**

5. **Hamburgers are usually made from which meat?**

6. **In aircrafts, what colour is the black box?**

7. **What type of creature is Bombay duck?**

8. **French horns originated from which country?**

# EIGHTIES JIG

Below are four of the biggest musical acts of the 1980s – a favourite era for many dads!

The names have been cut up, so all you have to do is piece the sections of letters together to reveal the answers.

MIC  MA  KI  DUR

HA  DON  SS  AN

EL  NA  CKS  DU

JA  ON  RAN

# WHAT COMES NEXT?

Here is a list of cryptic clues. Work out what they mean, and then you may be able to give the correct answer!

1 **LALD (1973)**

2 **TMWTGG**

3 **TSWLM**

4 **M (1979)**

What comes next, then?

# NO-GYM ABS

Dads like watching TV – that's hard to argue with! And most dads would like to attain a firmer midriff – again, undeniable! So why not combine the two? Here is a genius – and easy – hack for getting the latter while doing the former.

You see, the more a person is distracted, the more can be achieved without noticeable effort. When watching your favourite soap at home, you're more likely to exercise for longer than, say, when you're staring at a blank wall with no distraction (and this is why most people exercise while listening to music).

So, convert from a "couch potato" to a "soap exerciser" and see where this gets you after a few episodes. You'll be pleasantly surprised, even if you saw the cliffhanger coming.

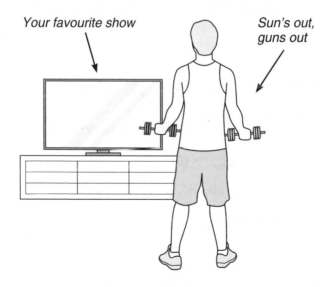

*Your favourite show*

*Sun's out, guns out*

# CROSSWORD: MALE SINGERS

Solve these clues to reveal the names of some famous male singers – some of which you may have impersonated badly!

1. Famous Frank found on a planet? (5, 4)

2. Not suitable for vegetarians (4, 4)

3. Average name, spaniel (3, 6)

4. To escort or steer (5)

5. Flintoff nickname, chemical element (7, 7)

6. Male ruler (6)

7. Filthy rivers, streams, etc. (5, 6)

8. Not slims, tile game (4, 6)

9. Not a "Dick" or "Harry", common surname (3, 5)

10. Scorpion weapon (5)

11. Name for "William", all at sea (5, 5)

12. Throw fruit (5, 5)

# DAD JOKES

**A MAN WAS OFFERED HIS DREAM JOB AT THE BRITTLE BONE SOCIETY FOR 100 GRAND A YEAR. HE SNAPPED THEIR HAND OFF.**

---

**WHENEVER MY WIFE, WHO'S AN ARTIST, IS SAD, I LET HER DRAW THINGS ON MY BODY. A SHOULDER TO CRAYON, SO TO SPEAK.**

---

**HOW DO YOU MAKE SEVEN EVEN? TAKE AWAY THE "S".**

# OBSCURE WORDS

Dads love all things literary, and what they love even more is learning the meaning of little-known words. These gems will have to be consigned to your "mental bank" for future use when you need some trivia to raise a few eyebrows!

**Preantepenultimate** – fourth from last (let's hope you aren't this in your next quiz!).

**Spraint** – otter dung

**Rowel** – the revolving star on the back of a cowboy's spurs

**Eugeria** – normal and happy old age (no comment!)

**Libberwort** – junk food

**Scroop** – the rustle of silk

**Peen** – the end of a hammer head opposite the striking face

**Fitch** – fur of a polecat/a small paintbrush

**Zarf** – a holder for a handleless coffee cup

**Ataxophobia** – fear of untidiness (given the state of their bedrooms, most children evidently don't suffer from this!).

**Ephebiphobia** – fear of teenagers or youths

# MISSING LETTER

Globetrotting dads should have no difficulty solving this one. Each of the following words is missing a letter; put all of them into the grid below to reveal a US city.

1 _OLD

2 DET_R

3 STE_M

4 ME_ER

5 DAR_

6 HO_E

7 FE_T

| 1 | 2 | 3 | 4 | 5 | 6 | 7 |
|---|---|---|---|---|---|---|
|   |   |   |   |   |   |   |

72

# SUDOKU

Fill in the rows with numbers from one to nine, but remember: each row, each column and each of the nine 3x3 squares must all contain the digits with no repeats.

| 8 |   |   |   |   |   |   |   |   |
|---|---|---|---|---|---|---|---|---|
|   |   |   |   | 8 | 3 |   |   |   |
|   | 7 | 3 |   |   | 6 | 5 |   | 9 |
| 2 |   |   |   | 4 | 7 |   | 1 | 5 |
|   |   | 5 | 8 |   | 2 | 6 |   |   |
| 7 | 4 |   | 5 | 1 |   |   |   | 3 |
| 9 |   | 1 | 3 |   |   | 2 | 4 |   |
|   |   |   | 7 | 5 |   |   |   |   |
|   |   |   |   |   |   |   |   | 6 |

# NO TEARS IN THE KITCHEN

Do you cry uncontrollably when chopping an onion? Then there are two tricks you might want to try. Unfortunately, these hacks won't help if you're crying because you've been asked to cook.

The first trick is to simply throw your onions in the freezer 30 minutes before you chop them. When you cut an onion, it starts to "bleed", releasing the irritant that makes us cry. Freezing them slows down this process, giving you a few precious minutes to chop, dry-eyed.

The second option is simply to move your chopping board underneath an extractor fan (make sure you switch it on, too). The fan will do what it says on the tin and extract the irritant from the air, leaving you free to cut your onion pieces precisely, with no need for a hankie!

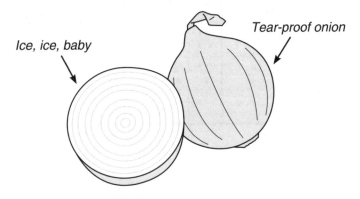

*Ice, ice, baby*

*Tear-proof onion*

# DAD JOKES

A MAN WENT TO HIS DOCTOR SUFFERING
FROM A FEAR OF STAIRLIFTS.
"THEY'RE ALWAYS UP TO
SOMETHING," HE CLAIMED.

---

WHY DO THE FRENCH HAVE
ONLY ONE EGG FOR BREAKFAST?
BECAUSE THAT'S *UN OEUF*.

---

MY FRIEND SAID SHE'S LEAVING HER
HUSBAND BECAUSE HE'S OBSESSED
WITH TENNIS AND HE'S TOO OLD.
WHEN SHE TOLD HIM, APPARENTLY HE
REPLIED, "I'M ONLY FORTY, LOVE."

# FASHION FACTS

Most dads think they're stylish, so here's a collection of trivia about fashion.

1. **Largest high-heeled shoe. Created by Dido Fashion Club, the dimensions of this gargantuan shoe are 3.96 metres (12 feet 11 inches) in length by 2.82 metres (9 feet 3 inches) in height.**

2. **Highest Mohican spike. Attention punk rockers! This record is currently a staggering 108.2 centimetres (42.5 inches) and belongs to the American Joseph Grisamore. How many jars of hair gel did he use?**

3. **Longest catwalk. Prepare yourself. Constructed in a Belgian shopping centre, the length of the world's longest catwalk is 2,292 metres (over 7,500 feet). It was used for a fashion show with 70 models. If you're wondering how long it would take a model to walk its entire length, it's 35 minutes!**

4. **And finally, most underpants put on in 30 seconds. Toshiaki Kasuga of Japan squeezed into 17 pairs of underpants in his permitted half-minute. What a guy!**

# WHIFFY UNDERPARTS

No doubt you consider yourself the picture of hygiene – and why wouldn't you? You're lovely! Honest…

However, the phenomenon of the stubborn "male stain" on the underarms of shirts is something that most of us can't escape. Think of the hours you put in during the day-to-day grind – it's only natural to develop pongy stains or a build-up of deodorant residue that are unsightly at best, and plain embarrassing at worst.

The solution comes in the form of vitamin C and $H_2O$. Scrub the stain with equal parts water and lemon juice, and then expose the offending shirt to heat – in the sun or on a radiator will do.

Now, that really is "easy-peasy, lemon squeezy".

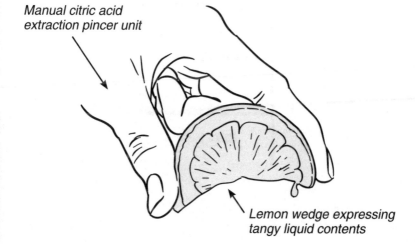

*Manual citric acid extraction pincer unit*

*Lemon wedge expressing tangy liquid contents*

# WORD LADDER

Solve this puzzle to get to a famous name in the sports world. Change one letter at a time to reveal the answer.

SILL

PELÉ

# EASY AS ABC?

ABC is usually child's play, but it's got to be harder than this for a dad. The first letters of each correct answer follow on from each other in alphabetical order. Just a hint: the answer to the first question doesn't start with an A!

1. What is the name of the landform at the mouth of a river created by the deposition of sediment?

2. What is the name of proteins that act as biological catalysts?

3. Which web browser was released in September 2002?

4. Who had a hit in 1978 with "I Will Survive"?

5. Who starred as Sam Spade in the 1941 film *The Maltese Falcon*?

6. Boise is the state capital of which US state?

7. Which is the oldest brother of the Jackson family – of The Jackson 5 fame?

# CROSSWORD

Dads love to do a spot of gardening. Test how green your fingers are with this crossword.

**1** To grow and to spring up (6)

**2** Broad flat leaf; species of newt (7)

**3** Underground stem (5)

**4** Plants native to mountains (7)

**5** Permanently verdant (9)

**6** Plant light? (4)

**7** Young plant (8)

**8** Coe, Cram or Ovett (6)

**9** Flower top not alive (8)

**10** Plant survives frost; Thomas's surname (5)

**11** Reproductive organ of a flower (6)

# LAST MEALS

Death row "last meals" hold a peculiar (or is that "morbid") fascination with a lot of people. Here are the final meal requests by four notorious murderers.

**Ted Bundy** – N/A. In fact, Bundy declined the usual personal request, so he was given the traditional last meal at the time of his execution. This consisted of: steak (medium rare), hash browns, eggs (over easy), toast (with butter and jelly/jam), juice and milk. Bundy wasn't hungry – he refused it.

**Fritz Haarmann ("The Butcher of Hanover")** – Brazilian coffee and a cigar.

**Stephen Wayne Anderson** – a pint of cottage cheese, grilled cheese sandwiches (he wasn't lactose-intolerant), corn mixture, radishes, chocolate-chip ice cream and peach pie.

**John Wayne Gacy** – 12 fried shrimps, French fries, a bucket of original recipe KFC (he had previously been the manager of three KFC stores) and 1 pound (453 grams) of strawberries.

# DAD JOKES

**WHAT DO YOU CALL A
COUPLE WHO LIKE FISHING?
ROD AND ANNETTE.**

---

**"DAD, CAN YOU PUT MY
SHOES ON?" ASKED JIMMY. DAD
LOOKED PUZZLED, THEN REPLIED,
"NO, JIMMY, THEY WON'T FIT ME!"**

# CLUED-UP

Work out the answers to the four clues below. They all have a connection – what is it?

1. **Louise Wener fronted this Britpop band.**

2. **50 per cent of Horatio?**

3. **Two large furry carnivores greet each other.**

4. **Three letters developed as an insecticide.**

# RUST-FREE DIY

Even if you're a modern sort of chap who's open to contemporary tips, some of the best pointers are tried and true. Enter the mothball.

Mothballs have been used for decades, and they have several uses. One of their lesser-known functions is to prevent metal from rusting. So, keep a few on hand (they're widely available in shops) and store them in your toolbox. Your tools' shelf life will increase, saving you a little bit of cash.

And here's one more nifty toolbox tip: now that your screws are safe from rust, try using a magnet to keep the smaller ones together.

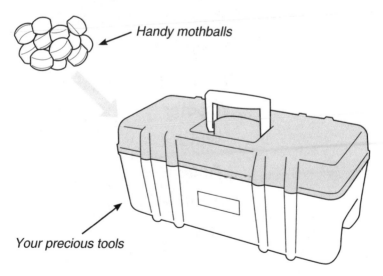

Handy mothballs

Your precious tools

# WORD SEARCH

A lot of dads enjoy the wonderful world of fishing. Find all the words below relating to angling. Just don't get "caught" out!

**Reel**

**Rod**

**Bait**

**Maggots**

**Waders**

**Umbrella**

**Tackle box**

**Cooler**

**Weight**

**Scales**

**Waterproofs**

**Flask**

```
L  H  V  V  G  H  A  Y  T  R  E  E  L  S  W
S  U  O  K  M  B  A  J  A  H  G  D  X  Y  A
J  N  M  A  G  G  O  T  S  D  A  D  C  Z  T
I  Y  G  B  B  J  K  P  L  K  H  H  U  T  E
F  E  F  D  R  X  V  E  R  N  K  O  S  L  R
W  Y  T  G  F  E  Z  E  U  H  B  R  H  N  P
E  H  Y  G  T  A  L  R  S  R  E  G  H  I  R
I  J  J  C  I  O  D  L  S  D  H  I  O  R  O
G  B  H  F  O  S  R  G  A  H  V  X  G  O  O
H  S  V  C  J  O  K  W  G  F  D  S  T  D  F
T  C  L  K  H  G  Y  U  F  S  A  Z  B  Q  S
A  A  P  X  T  A  C  K  L  E  B  O  X  H  G
F  L  A  S  K  A  S  K  L  N  V  C  R  P  K
J  E  C  C  G  D  S  E  F  Y  B  A  I  T  A
X  S  H  G  F  T  U  N  M  K  U  O  P  A  P
```

# BANKING ON AN ACTING CAREER

Like most dads, you'll appreciate the skills of a talented actor – and there aren't many who are more talented (or perhaps more beautiful) than South African Charlize Theron. But how was she discovered?

It all came down to her kicking up a stink in a Hollywood Boulevard bank. In 1994, the then 19-year-old Ms Theron strolled into the bank, where a teller refused to cash her out-of-state cheque. The would-be actor complained with, one might imagine, a theatrical tantrum. Guess who was standing in the queue nearby? Only veteran talent manager John Crosby, who was impressed with her outburst and promptly gave her his business card.

The rest is history, with Ms Theron winning Best Actress at the Oscars for her lead role in *Monster*.

Should you be throwing a tantrum in public? Hmm… not really, but if it results in being a Hollywood A-lister, why not?!

# SPORT ONE TO TEN

Each answer to this sports quiz is a number from one to ten, but they can only be used once!

1. The USA was the host country for the FIFA World Cup in the year 199... ?

2. How many players are there on an ice-hockey team (on the ice)?

3. In the 2020/21 Premiership table, how many teams end with a vowel?

4. On a dartboard, which number comes in-between 20 and 18?

5. In rugby union, a hooker usually wears which shirt number?

6. How many times has Martina Navratilova been Wimbledon Ladies' Singles champion?

7. The width of the goalposts in football is how many yards?

8. Each hole at the Augusta National Golf Club in Georgia is famously named after a tree or shrub. What is the number of the hole named Camellia?

9. Henry Cooper won his first BBC Sports Personality of the Year award in the year 196...?

10. In snooker, the blue ball is worth how many points?

# SUDOKU

Fill in the rows with numbers from one to nine, but remember: each row, each column and each of the nine 3x3 squares must all contain the digits with no repeats.

| 1 |   |   |   |   |   |   |   |   |
|---|---|---|---|---|---|---|---|---|
|   |   | 9 |   |   |   |   | 2 | 3 |
|   |   |   |   | 7 | 6 |   | 1 |   |
| 3 |   |   |   | 1 |   |   |   | 8 |
|   |   | 7 | 9 | 3 | 8 | 6 |   |   |
| 5 |   |   |   | 2 |   |   |   | 9 |
|   | 3 |   | 5 | 4 |   |   |   |   |
| 6 | 1 |   |   |   |   | 8 |   |   |
|   |   |   |   |   |   |   |   | 2 |

# IN A RIGHT STATE

Starting with the letter in bold and moving one letter at a time, either vertically or horizontally, find four US states. The last letter of each word is the first letter of the next. Don't get lost!

| I | L | L | I | C | U | T |
|---|---|---|---|---|---|---|
| D | A | H | Y | K | E | N |
| I | E | O | I | A | K | O |
| H | E | R | A | O | R | B |
| I | G | I | W | Y | C | A |
| S | O | N | E | A | T | W |
| E | A | S | I | O | P | A |

# DAD JOKE

I WENT TO SEE AN AIR SHOW TODAY. THERE WERE LOTS OF "OOHS" AND "AAHS" AS THE CROWD WATCHED IN AMAZEMENT. NEAR MISS AFTER NEAR MISS HAD PEOPLE COVERING THEIR EYES AND SHAKING THEIR HEADS IN DISBELIEF. IT WAS A GOOD HALF HOUR'S WORTH OF ENTERTAINMENT, BUT IN THE END, MY FRIEND TOM FINALLY MANAGED TO PARK THE CAR AND WE MADE OUR WAY TO THE AIR SHOW.

# NAILING IT

Hammer? Check. Nail? Check. Wood… check for cracks.

Why? Because wood with cracks tends to split, and so your nail might cause the wood to completely erupt.

If the wood does have cracks, try this. With the hammer and nail, make a small "starting hole" about two centimetres (an inch) in depth, and then extract the nail and dip it in paraffin. Once that is done, continue: hammer away and the nail should go into the wood smoothly. Run out of paraffin? Rubbing the nail with soap will produce similar results!

*Paraffin*

*Lubricate that nail*

# FOOTBALL TRIVIA

Think you know your football? If you do, you might know that the most capped male footballer for their country is Bader Al-Mutawa with 185 caps for Kuwait. But this impressive figure is nowhere near the most capped footballer of all time. The title belongs to American footballer Kristine Lilly, who amassed an astonishing 354 caps between 1987 and 2010.

Here are some more football stats to impress your friends...

**1** **The two closest professional football stadiums in the UK are those belonging to Dundee and Dundee United. They are roughly just 200 metres (650 yards) apart.**

**2** **Swedish footballer Stefan Schwarz once had a contract that prohibited him from travelling into space (that's interplanetary space, not the space inside the 12-yard box!)**

**3** **Goalkeeper Tim Wiese became a WWE wrestler.**

**4** **One of Atlético Madrid's nicknames is *Los Colchoneros*, meaning "The Mattress Makers", because the first team stripes were the same colour as traditional Spanish mattresses.**

**5** **While in charge of Arsenal, Arsène Wenger signed a total of 126 players.**

# WHAT COMES NEXT?

What comes sixth in the following sequence?

1 **Athens (1896)**

2 **Paris (1900)**

3 **St Louis (1904)**

4 **London (1908)**

5 **Stockholm (1912)**

6 **…?**

# WHO AM I?

See how many clues it takes you to reveal the identity of the mystery person.

**1** **I was born in the US state of Georgia in 1953.**

**2** **In 2008, my estimated net worth was $30 million.**

**3** **My real name is Terry Bollea.**

**4** **I made an appearance in *Rocky III*.**

**5** **I am most well-known as a wrestler.**

# WALLPAPER FIASCOS

Let's face it: wallpapering is one of those jobs where hope turns to frustration in the blink of an eye… and often ends up in resignation even quicker than that.

Commit these three tips to memory, though, and the whole experience should be that little bit easier.

**1** **To remove painted wallpaper more easily, take a wire brush dipped in water and gently rub over the surface; this allows water to soak in.**

**2** **Add a tablespoonful of baking soda to every bucket of warm water you use when stripping wallpaper (a mixture of paste, water and liquid detergent is also effective).**

**3** **Write down on the wall the quantities of wallpaper used to decorate a room, before you finish papering. Next time you strip the walls, there's no need to measure!**

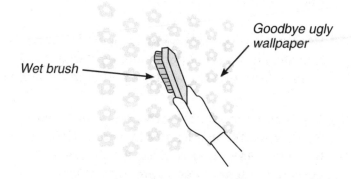

*Goodbye ugly wallpaper*

*Wet brush*

# ZOOS

Sons, daughters and grandchildren often beg to be taken to the zoo. Well, animal parks are great go-to tourist attractions, and let's not pretend that you don't enjoy it, too! Show off your zoo(ological) knowledge with these facts.

1. In terms of species, the world's largest zoo is in Moscow (Moskovsky Zoopark). As of late 2020, the zoo housed 1,226 species of animals – considerably more than the number in London Zoo. The species list includes giraffe (tallest animal), Chinese alligator (smallest crocodilian), peregrine falcon (fastest animal), reticulated python (longest snake), moose (largest deer) and African giant millipede (most legs on an animal).

2. The most visited zoo is Disney's Animal Kingdom in Florida, which saw 13.9 million people in 2019.

3. Inhabiting the largest penguin pool in Europe, Sir Nils Olav is a king penguin and was knighted in 2008 in front of 130 guardsman at Edinburgh Zoo.

4. The world's most northerly zoo is the Polar Park Arctic Wildlife Centre in Bardu, Norway. No, there aren't any species that thrive in the sunshine! (Just in case your kids ask...)

# DAD JOKES

*A CROOK WAS CAUGHT
STEALING A CALENDAR.
HE GOT 12 MONTHS.*

---

*THE WORLD TONGUE-TWISTER
CHAMPION WAS ARRESTED RECENTLY.
SHE GOT A TOUGH SENTENCE.*

---

*ANOTHER MAN WAS ARRESTED
FOR STEALING FIREWORKS.
HOWEVER, HE WAS LET OFF.*

---

*MEANWHILE, A WOMAN WAS ARRESTED
FOR STEALING A CHEESE TOASTIE.
THE POLICE REALLY GRILLED HER.*

# CAMP IT UP!

Starting with the letter in bold and moving one letter at a time, either vertically or horizontally, find four items you might take on a camping trip. The last letter of each word is the first letter of the next.

| F | L | I | G | H | T | I |
|---|---|---|---|---|---|---|
| A | A | S | A | P | O | F |
| O | B | H | D | D | N | T |
| I | S | L | I | T | E | O |
| D | A | C | G | H | L | I |
| D | R | E | C | T | E | W |
| S | S | P | A | P | S | A |

# LETTER LINK

Below are four pairs of clues. There is only *one* letter present in *both* answers. The four letters then spell a male Christian name.

1. Newcastle brown beer and heaviest snake

2. Homer's favourite beer and the sport played by James Wade

3. Turkey's capital and comedy partner of Hale

4. LA American football team and tenth most populated country

# DON'T FORGET TO WATER THE PLANTS!

You're going on a well-deserved holiday – bravo! – and so you've asked the neighbours to put your bins out and keep an eye out for irksome loiterers.

But the indoor plants! Who's going to water them? You'd prefer not to give anyone your house keys, so there's only one solution to this horticultural quandary.

Place a container of water near your plants. Next, find some lengths of chunky wool. Place one end of each piece of wool in the water container, and the other ends in each of the flowerpots. The sturdy wool will absorb the water that, in turn, will trickle into the pots. This simple operation will elevate your status from green-fingered amateur to green-fingered indoor-plant maestro.

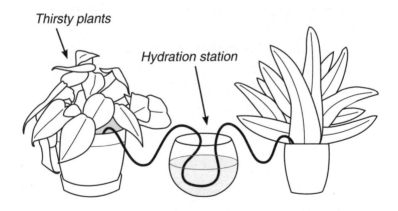

*Thirsty plants*

*Hydration station*

# DO IT YOURSELF

Below is a tool often used in DIY, but what is it? You'll get no indication of the number of words, although the letters are in the correct order.

| | D | | U | | T | A | | L | | W | | | N | C | |

# WOMEN OF THE BIG SCREEN

If you consider yourself a film buff then you should make short work of this quiz. Here are eight questions on some well-known ladies to test your knowledge.

1. Who played Mikaela in the 2007 film *Transformers*?

2. In which film did Hilary Swank play Maggie Fitzgerald?

3. Who played Princess Leia in the original *Star Wars* films?

4. Which famous woman was on the front cover of the first *Playboy* magazine?

5. Who was the leading lady in the 2003 film *Girl with a Pearl Earring*?

6. Which actor said that if they had a day off from being a celebrity, they'd love to go to a mosh pit at a rock concert?

7. Who played Carrie Bradshaw in *Sex and the City*?

8. Which actor was the first lady to be "killed" in the 1996 film *Scream*?

# ANAGRAM

This is a tough one, but for super-dads it can easily be conquered! The cryptic clue is: far too early to imbibe this?

# NURSE QUALITIES

# WORD SEARCH

Enjoy tinkering in the garage? Use your wits to find all the words below – most of these will have been in your garage at one time or another!

**Battery**

**Washers**

**Spanner**

**Oil can**

**Paint**

**Flowerpot**

**Glass cleaner**

**Dustpan**

**Overalls**

**Spiderweb**

**Ladder**

**Car**

**Bicycle**

| | | | | | | | | | | | | | | |
|---|---|---|---|---|---|---|---|---|---|---|---|---|---|---|
| A | P | J | H | F | L | O | W | E | R | P | O | T | A | O |
| M | H | G | F | D | E | H | T | B | A | T | T | E | R | Y |
| G | O | B | E | G | A | T | A | G | C | S | A | A | J | B |
| V | V | J | I | A | M | Y | U | J | K | L | N | A | G | S |
| A | E | G | Y | C | J | I | J | H | V | N | F | R | W | P |
| F | R | I | A | M | Y | B | J | K | A | K | H | G | F | I |
| A | A | E | D | T | F | C | V | C | U | J | K | L | A | D |
| J | L | V | U | R | A | A | L | T | N | L | O | A | J | E |
| W | L | J | S | B | G | I | S | E | Y | I | O | D | H | R |
| A | S | R | T | W | O | X | F | G | H | J | K | D | N | W |
| S | T | G | P | J | I | K | A | P | K | H | B | E | Y | E |
| H | G | L | A | S | S | C | L | E | A | N | E | R | V | B |
| E | E | R | N | F | S | A | K | P | L | O | H | G | B | N |
| R | H | F | D | R | S | S | A | E | R | F | D | C | A | R |
| S | P | A | N | N | E | R | A | P | P | A | I | N | T | S |

107

# DAD JOKES

**NEWS JUST IN! THE LOCAL PROCRASTINATION CLUB MEETING HAS BEEN POSTPONED UNTIL NEXT WEEK.**

---

**I WAS GOING TO JOIN THE DEBATING TEAM, BUT SOMEBODY TALKED ME OUT OF IT.**

---

**A WOMAN WAS SEEN PUTTING FLYERS ABOUT DRIED GRAPES THROUGH PEOPLE'S LETTER BOXES. WHEN ASKED, SHE SAID SHE WAS JUST RAISIN AWARENESS.**

# GOLFING BIRDIES

Which dad hasn't played at least one round of golf? There's nothing better than teeing off on a sunny day, trying to reduce a handicap and regaling each other with golfing stories on the "nineteenth hole".

Most golfers know about the terms used when everything is going well:

**Par** – a hole score equal to the "par" of that hole, i.e. the same number of strokes a proficient golfer should need to complete the hole.

**Birdie** – a hole score of **one** stroke fewer than par.

**Eagle** – a hole score of **two** strokes fewer than par.

**Albatross** – a hole score of **three** strokes fewer than par (this is rare indeed, as it would be a hole-in-one on a par-four hole).

But have you ever heard of a golfer attaining a hole score of *four* strokes fewer than par? That means a hole-in-one on a par-five hole, or someone who has completed a par-six hole in just two strokes. Well, this is *exceedingly* rare and has only been recorded a handful of times. The achievement is often aided by high altitudes, and its "unofficial" name is a **condor**. Bet you didn't know that!

# ANAGRAMS

Clean shaven or lusciously bearded, dads take pride in their hair – whether it's facial or on top! Unscramble items you may find in a traditional barber's – chop-chop!

1. **PILPCERS**

2. **TITZ RAGS HORAR**

3. **YAH REDIRR**

4. **MITRE MRS**

5. **MOPEDA**

6. **LEG**

# UNRAVELLING THE EARPHONE DILEMMA

If there's one fact that dads know all too well (other than that they'll forget to put the rubbish out at least *once* in their life), it's that earphones are not immune to knots. In fact, sometimes that's *all* they tend to do – as if they tangle on purpose.

Combat this exasperating conundrum by using a humble tape dispenser. Simply reel your earphone wires onto the tape ring, leaving the connector ("jack") showing at the back, and the earbuds at the front. It's not quite as fashionable as other gadgets, but you're a dad: practicality trumps style every time!

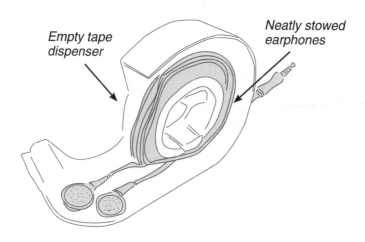

*Empty tape dispenser*

*Neatly stowed earphones*

# ❓
# SPORTING NICKNAMES

Here are ten nicknames of famous sportsmen. To help you along your way, you've generously been given the sport they're famous for playing.

1. **"White Lightning" – cricket**

2. **"A-Rod" – tennis**

3. **"The Machine" – darts**

4. **"Refrigerator"/"The Fridge" – American football**

5. **"The Big Easy" – golf**

6. **"The Fun Bus" – rugby union**

7. **"Il Divin Codino" (Italian for "The Divine Ponytail") – football**

8. **"Angles" – snooker**

9. **"Chariots" – rugby league**

10. **"Daffy" – cricket**

# DAD JOKES

*HOW DO YOU KILL A CIRCUS?*
*GO STRAIGHT FOR THE JUGGLER.*

---

*NEVER TRUST ATOMS –*
*THEY MAKE EVERYTHING UP.*

---

*WHAT'S ET SHORT FOR?*
*BECAUSE HE'S ONLY GOT LITTLE LEGS!*

# SLUSHY MOTORWAY

Dads often enjoy a good read, and literature trivia even more so! If you're a fan of Mills & Boon, perhaps you should look away now.

These books were creatively put to use in 2003 when nearly 2.5 million copies were pulped and used as an absorbent top layer of the M6 motorway in the UK.

The "pulp" fiction helped to hold the tarmac and asphalt in place, and also acted as a sound absorber. For every mile (roughly every two kilometres) of the motorway, approximately 45,000 books were required.

A spokesman commented, "We used copies of Mills & Boon books, not as a statement about what we think of the writing, but because it is so absorbent. They may be slushy to many people, but it's their 'no-slushiness' that is their attraction, as far as we were concerned."

Think about it the next time you're driving to work or taking the family on a jaunt. What *else* could you be driving on?

# WORD LADDER

Change one letter at a time to get to this four-letter word associated with golf. Don't get lost in the rough!

COLD

HOLE

# NATIONAL DISHES

Work up an appetite by answering these food-related questions. We've given you the name of the dish, so all you need to do is work out the corresponding country the food is most associated with.

1 **Moussaka**

2 **Sushi**

3 **Taco**

4 **Nasi goreng**

5 **Jerk chicken**

6 **Ceviche**

7 **Borscht**

8 **Kabsa**

9 **Tortilla de patatas**

10 **Tom yum**

# NICE PAIR!

Each word in the right-hand column below can be paired with one word from the left-hand column to form a longer word. Then, when the eight longer words are placed correctly in the grid, a man's name appears in the shaded column. What is it? (It could be your own!)

ODOUR LIGHT

AMID NAMED

NICK SHIPS

LAMP STYLE

HAIR WORK

DART RING

REFER BOARD

PAINT LESS

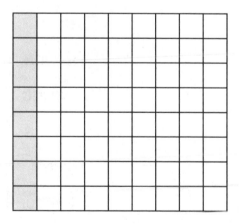

# VOWEL CAN YOU WORK THESE OUT?

You don't have to be a talented musician to work out these answers. The vowels from the following musical instruments have been deleted. See how many instruments you can get!

1 CLL

2 KLL

3 CCRDN

4 HRMNC

5 TMBRN

6 MRMB

7 HRPSCHRD

8 LCTRC GTR

9 B

# DAD JOKES

**DAD: WHERE WERE THESE
FRENCH FRIES COOKED?
KID: FRANCE?
DAD: NOPE — THEY WERE
COOKED IN GREECE.**

---

**HAVE YOU READ THE BOOK
ABOUT ANTI-GRAVITY?
IT'S IMPOSSIBLE TO PUT DOWN.**

---

**I TIME-TRAVELLED INTO THE PAST SO I
COULD DECORATE MY BEDROOM PINK.
THEN I WENT BACK TO THE FUCHSIA.**

# NICE ONE, EINSTEIN!

Here's some trivia for the science-loving dads. You'll probably remember some basic scientific facts from school, but how about these lesser-known nuggets of information?

1. **The average human adult body contains about 100 trillion cells.**

2. **The pH scale – which measures acidity or alkalinity of substances – means "power (or potential) of hydrogen". It measures the concentration of hydrogen ions.**

3. **What do 20,000 tonnes of TNT and one kilogram of plutonium have in common? They would both produce the same explosion, of course. Boom!**

4. **Butterflies drink crocodile tears for nutrition.**

5. **There are more atoms in a teaspoonful of water than there are teaspoonfuls of water in the Atlantic Ocean.**

6. **An average human heart beats 100,000 times a day.**

7. **The dwarf planet Pluto has a heart-shaped glacier over 1,000 kilometres (621 miles) in length.**

# FILM BUFF

Starting with the letter in bold and moving one letter at a time, either vertically or horizontally, find four surnames of famous actors. The last letter of each word is the first letter of the next. Even Barry Norman would find this a challenge!

| F | O | R | Y | T | E | L |
|---|---|---|---|---|---|---|
| I | E | D | M | E | M | A |
| D | M | A | P | C | S | L |
| B | O | N | E | E | U | J |
| F | U | O | B | S | O | U |
| E | S | L | K | I | N | E |
| N | O | O | H | C | B | Y |

# SUDOKU

Fill in the rows with numbers from one to nine, but remember: each row, each column and each of the nine 3x3 squares must all contain the digits with no repeats.

|   |   |   |   |   | 5 |   |   |   |
|---|---|---|---|---|---|---|---|---|
|   |   |   | 3 |   |   | 1 | 6 |   |
|   |   | 6 |   | 4 | 7 | 5 |   | 3 |
|   | 6 | 8 |   | 7 | 4 |   |   |   |
|   |   | 9 | 5 |   |   |   | 8 | 2 |
|   | 3 | 5 |   | 6 | 9 |   |   |   |
|   |   | 1 |   | 3 | 6 | 7 |   | 5 |
|   |   |   | 4 |   |   | 2 | 9 |   |
|   |   |   |   | 2 |   |   |   |   |

# KEEP THE FIZZ GOING

Most dads can't bear to see things going to waste, and this especially applies to a perfectly chilled bottle of beer.

On the off-chance that you don't want to finish your refreshing bottle of brew, here's a handy tip to keep the liquid refreshment fizzy. All you need to do is pour the leftover beer into a screw-top bottle, secure the cap on tightly and then put the bottle in your fridge *upside down*. Carbonation time varies, but the beer should stay fizzy for at least several hours – if not a few days.

Failing that, don't be a fizzy rascal, and just finish the beer in the way it's intended!

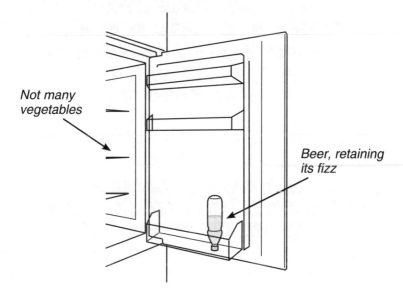

*Not many vegetables*

*Beer, retaining its fizz*

# DAD JOKES

A SLICE OF APPLE PIE IS $3 IN
THE BAHAMAS AND $2.50 IN JAMAICA.
THESE ARE THE PIE RATES OF
THE CARIBBEAN...

---

MY FRIEND KEEPS SAYING,
"CHEER UP, IT COULD BE WORSE.
YOU COULD BE STUCK UNDERGROUND
IN A POOL OF WATER."
I KNOW HE MEANS WELL.

---

WHY CAN'T YOU HEAR A
PTERODACTYL USING THE BATHROOM?
BECAUSE THE "P" IS SILENT.

# MULTIPLE ANSWERS

Grab yourself a piece of paper long enough to write down 28 answers! See if you can get them all.

**1** **Name the three films with one-word titles that won Best Picture at the Oscars in the 1990s.**

**2** **According to CBS News, name the top eight most common passwords in 2013 (for technology appliances like laptops, phones, etc.).**

**3** **As the crow flies, name the five closest capital cities to Moscow.**

**4** **Name the five plays by Shakespeare that begin with vowels.**

# DAD JOKES

## THERE ARE THREE UNWRITTEN RULES OF LIFE:

1. _____

2. _____

3. _____

_____

**DO YOU WANT TO HEAR A WORD I JUST MADE UP? PLAGIARISM.**

_____

**RIP, BOILED WATER. YOU WILL BE MIST.**

# HAPPY JOBS

Do you know what the "happiest" professions are? In 2020 to celebrate International Week of Happiness at Work, 40,000 UK professionals were surveyed to find out the answer. Here are the top ten professions that make workers "very happy". Whether you peruse this with interest or use it as a checklist for your next job hunt is up to you.

1. **Landscapers**
2. **Dog walkers**
3. **Counsellors**
4. **Wedding photographers**
5. **Architects**
6. **Tutors**
7. **Tennis coaches**
8. **Ski instructors**
9. **Gardeners**
10. **Personal trainers**

# NO MORE KEY-RING CALAMITIES

Who likes fiddly things? No one, that's who. Unfortunately, some things just *are* fiddly, and near the top of most men's lists of these dreaded items are undoubtedly key rings, which are useful and infuriating in equal measure.

But they needn't be! To minimize complicated finger gymnastics, key-ring users should have a handy pair of staple removers with them at all times. Simply use their prongs to separate the key-ring segments for a fiddle-free operation. Plus, you'll have no more broken fingernails!

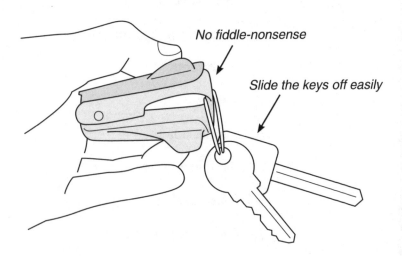

*No fiddle-nonsense*

*Slide the keys off easily*

# VOWEL CAN YOU WORK THESE OUT?

Impress everyone (even your family!) by working out the capital cities below, whose vowels have been taken out. Sneakily, they'll get more difficult as you progress around the world.

1. **PRS**

2. **MDRD**

3. **NKR**

4. **BNS RS**

5. **ISLMBD**

6. **TTW**

7. **SL**

8. **MGDSH**

9. **MPT**

10. **BNJL**

11. **NTNNRV**

12. **GDG**

# HOLIDAY ANAGRAMS

Below are five anagrams relating to holidays. Even though you're undoubtedly a busy dad, you must know what a holiday is!

1 **NUS GUNLOER**

2 **PORSTAPS**

3 **FISTR SLACS**

4 **ROBDINGA SAPS**

5 **CAFE KASM**

# CRYPTIC CLUES

There are two answers to each pair of clues, and they differ by just one letter. Stop scratching your head and get cracking!

1. Venomous snake and music genre/dance.

2. Combustible sedimentary rock and to persuade.

3. Bed covering and to have constructed.

4. Famous cartoon mouse, and a fruit with seeds and pulp.

5. And one with a triplet of clues: young horse, an unfair sporting act and "disgusting" chicken.

# MOTH-FREE CLOTHES

Keeping your favourite shirts and suits in one piece is simple, right?

Well, of course it is – providing you've grasped the basic concept of clothes hangers, because it's their material that can help to deter moths.

Opt for wooden hangers made from cedar. The oils in it are rich in types of hydrocarbon, which give off a lingering "resinous" aroma that sees off adult moths – the ones that could lay eggs on your clothes and leave their larva to have a free lunch when hatched.

Another way to keep the moths away is to keep all environs around your clothes dust-free – you know where the vacuum is!

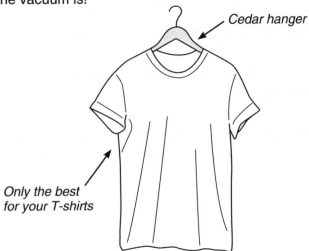

*Cedar hanger*

*Only the best for your T-shirts*

# RUGBY-UNION TRIVIA

Do you enjoy watching 30 men in shorts getting muddy and tackling each other? Each to their own! Here are some facts about the game's history.

1. The value of a try in rugby union is five points, although this was only established in 1992. Previously, a try was worth four points, three, two, one and even zero...

2. The capacity of Twickenham Stadium in London is greater than that of the population of the suburban town of Twickenham.

3. A rugby ball is oval-shaped because pigs' bladders were originally used as the material to make them. Times have changed now, of course!

4. The world television audience for the inaugural Rugby World Cup in 1987 was 300 million. By 2007, that figure was 4.2 billion!

5. The same whistle is blown by referees for the opening game at each Rugby World Cup tournament. The item is called the Gil Evans whistle – named after a Welsh ref who first used the shrill instrument in 1905.

# OPPOSITES ATTRACT

Are you an intelligent dad one day and a daft one on another? Sort each set of the letter blocks into two words with opposite meanings.

**1** DA AR UN SC NT AB CE

**2** OM VI ED CAP FRE TY TI

**3** HT RA BE ST ND EN IG

# OIL CHANGE EYE-OPENER

Don your overalls – it's time to check the oil in your lawnmower. From experience, you know it's a tricky task to complete without even the smallest of spillages.

That's because you haven't reached for an empty box of breakfast cereal recently! You see, most cereal boxes have a glossy finish to the cardboard packaging. This means you can cut off a piece and form a trough to guide the oil from your lawnmower into a container. The glossy coating prevents any liquid from seeping through, giving you a precise oil-changing channel. Great, huh?

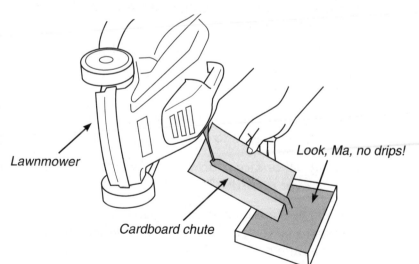

Lawnmower

Look, Ma, no drips!

Cardboard chute

# RECORD-BREAKERS

Every dad loves a stat. Here are eight questions inspired by world records: see how close you get to the correct answers (you won't be "spot on" on many!).

1. In metres or feet, how tall is the tallest building in the world?

2. In hours, how long was the longest cricket net session by an individual?

3. In metres or feet, how high was the tallest wave surfed?

4. In metres or feet, how long was the longest wedding dress train?

5. When measured in 2019, how tall in metres or feet was the tallest living tree – a redwood nicknamed Hyperion?

6. The oldest person ever to have been fully authenticated lived to how many years?

7. In kilogram or stone, how heavy was the heaviest human ever recorded?

8. The Black Diamonds were the youngest professional rock band when they released their debut album in 2010. What was their average age?

# DAD JOKES

WHAT DO YOU CALL CHEESE
THAT'S NOT YOURS?
NACHO CHEESE.

---

ON WHICH CHANNEL ARE THE WORLD
ORIGAMI CHAMPIONSHIPS SHOWN?
PAPER VIEW.

---

WHAT'S THE BEST PART
ABOUT LIVING IN SWITZERLAND?
WHO KNOWS — BUT ITS
FLAG IS A BIG PLUS.

**?**

# NUMBERS GAME

Many dads are great with digits, but will you pick the correct numbers for each of these questions? If you don't know… guess!

1. For how many years of marriage is a "Ruby" wedding anniversary celebrated?

2. How many squares on a chessboard are occupied by chess pieces at the start of a game of chess?

3. How many US states begin with the letter "O"?

4. How many members are in the Backstreet Boys?

5. A regular bar billiards table comprises how many holes?

6. What number is a hurricane represented by on the Beaufort scale?

7. In Roman numerals, what number is CD?

8. How many zeros are there in one trillion (on the "short scale" in British and American definitions)

# FOUR BY FOUR

Get cracking with this mini crossword – it's small, but perfectly formed!

| 1 | 2 | 3 | 4 |
|---|---|---|---|
| 5 |   |   |   |
| 6 |   |   |   |
| 7 |   |   |   |

**ACROSS**

**1** Washtub

**5** Region/zone

**6** Deceiver

**7** "Truth or..."

**DOWN**

**1** Lacking hair

**2** Vocal solo in opera

**3** Produced by the lacrimal gland

**4** Adult leveret

# WHAT'S PUZZLING ON THE BBQ?

Starting with the letter in bold and moving one letter at a time, either vertically or horizontally, find four items that can be used during a family barbecue. The last letter of each word is the first letter of the next. Note – only two of the four items are edible!

| **A** | P | E | G | E | S | T |
|---|---|---|---|---|---|---|
| L | R | A | A | S | O | E |
| K | O | N | O | U | K | A |
| M | C | A | J | A | F | D |
| M | N | P | K | S | O | P |
| E | I | D | I | N | G | G |
| T | R | P | A | Q | U | D |

# LAWNMOWER HELPING HAND

Keeping one's lawn in pristine condition is one of life's pleasures – especially to a proud dad. However, it's not all plain sailing. Many dads have to deal with weeds, twigs and other debris, and often throw these unsightly items in a flower bed to be picked up later on.

But why waste time? Fasten cardboard or plastic containers to your mower with masking tape, and throw weeds and other detritus into them as you go along. Then, when your lawn finally has faultless green stripes, unfasten the containers and empty them into a bin. No more combing the area for thrown-away debris!

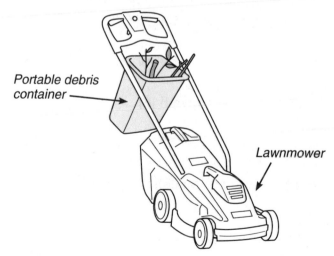

Portable debris container —

Lawnmower

# CROSSWORD: IN THE BAR

Fancy an hour or two in your local? Of course you do! Test your knowledge of public bars with this crossword.

1 **Time please, gentlemen! (4, 6)**

2 **Drinking vessel holding 20 imperial fluid ounces/16 US fluid ounces (4, 5)**

3 **Lager wipes its feet on this? (4, 3)**

4 **Without her, you won't be served! (7)**

5 **She who must be obeyed! (8)**

6 **Wild West bar (6)**

7 **Come here often? You definitely do! (7)**

# ANAGRAM

This is two puzzles in one. First, answer all the questions below and then decode the anagram: by rearranging the first letter of each of the five correct answers, you'll spell the surname of a famous sportsman.

1. Tallinn is the capital city of which European country?

2. Which 1995 thriller starred Morgan Freeman, Brad Pitt and Gwyneth Paltrow?

3. Which is the world's second-largest religion, with a reputed 1.8 billion followers?

4. Which famous sportsman was born Cassius Clay in 1942?

5. Ted Lowe was a well-known commentator of which sport?

# DAD JOKES

**WHAT DO YOU CALL
A WOMAN WITH ONE LEG
LONGER THAN THE OTHER?
EILEEN.**

---

**WHICH CHEESE IS
MADE BACKWARDS?
EDAM.**

---

**WHICH DOG IS THE
BEST AT MAGIC TRICKS?
A LABRACADABRADOR.**

# OLYMPIC BOOZING

Here's a little-known slice of sporting trivia that dads can use to impress friends, co-workers and fellow parents.

The first athlete to be disqualified at the Olympics for drug use was Swedish modern pentathlete Hans-Gunnar Liljenwall, at the 1968 Summer Olympics in Mexico City. But for which substance did Mr Liljenwall test positive, resulting in the disqualification of the entire Swedish pentathlon team? Steroids? Cocaine? Painkillers?

Nope. In fact, the offending substance was ethanol. That's alcohol, to many. The nervous Swede consumed "two beers" to steady his nerves prior to the pistol-shooting event (which must have reassured the spectators!).

Though alcohol has many side effects (impairing coordination, clouding judgement, etc.), there is a popular idea that it gives an advantage. How? The hypothesis is that alcohol could potentially improve performances in individuals prone to stress or overthinking!

# SPORTS MAD

Starting with the letter in bold and moving one letter at a time, either vertically or horizontally, find four pieces of sporting equipment. The last letter of each word is the first letter of the next. Just don't smash your racquet if you get stumped!

| **B** | O | G | G | D | O | C |
|---|---|---|---|---|---|---|
| A | I | C | E | K | D | R |
| C | L | A | B | G | O | A |
| G | S | L | J | T | B | M |
| O | H | L | A | R | E | S |
| T | I | N | D | I | F | N |
| O | T | P | A | D | O | M |

# RIDDLE ME THIS...

Put your "dad brain" in gear to solve this tricky riddle.

**Delete one letter from the ninth animal
in the Chinese zodiac to get your fortune.
"Multiply" the word three times. Reverse
the name of the band who released this in
1976. Which four letters do you have?**

# MISSING LETTER

Popcorn at the ready! Each of the following words is missing a letter. Put them into the grid below to reveal a film which has grossed over $1 billion.

1. TA_TE

2. JO_ES

3. BOD_

4. _ALLS

5. SH_VE

6. RO_E

7. HE_PS

| 1 | 2 | 3 | 4 | 5 | 6 | 7 |
|---|---|---|---|---|---|---|
|   |   |   |   |   |   |   |

# WORD SEARCH

If your bedroom is as clean as your children's, you probably won't be able to find the items in this tricky grid!

**Slippers**

**Dressing gown**

**Lamp**

**Books**

**Comb**

**Hairbrush**

**Alarm clock**

**Mirror**

**Wardrobe**

**Toiletries**

**Pyjamas**

**Towel**

```
L  F  C  W  A  R  D  R  O  B  E  E  F  D  A
A  K  M  N  H  U  J  G  C  F  D  R  E  W  L
D  G  D  R  E  S  S  I  N  G  G  O  W  N  A
V  X  X  D  R  L  I  O  P  K  J  H  G  T  R
A  D  F  G  T  I  E  W  S  L  A  M  P  H  M
C  K  J  G  G  P  R  E  W  D  S  J  H  P  C
O  K  O  I  J  P  Y  G  F  K  E  Y  A  Y  L
M  K  F  R  E  E  P  L  O  N  G  Y  F  J  O
B  I  G  J  O  R  M  O  G  H  Y  T  U  A  C
K  U  R  R  E  S  B  C  H  T  I  J  J  M  K
Y  G  H  R  C  X  S  E  R  D  O  O  H  A  K
A  V  B  H  O  F  D  A  S  W  T  W  H  S  V
C  F  H  A  I  R  B  R  U  S  H  J  E  Y  G
F  D  W  W  S  D  G  H  T  R  F  C  X  L  A
T  O  I  L  E  T  R  I  E  S  P  L  M  N  D
```

# SAVE YOUR BACK
# WHEN RAKING

Raking is one of those jobs that often fall to dads to tick off the "to-do list". Although it's not particularly difficult, it's definitely much harder on the back than it looks. Back-breaking, so to speak.

To minimize aches and pains when raking, find a short section of plastic pipe with a tee fitting. Feed this section over your rake handle, with the tee facing up, so that it will act as a second handle. This will provide much-needed relief for your lower back and should also increase your raking efficiency! If the piping wobbles slightly, simply screw it into the rake handle. Job done!

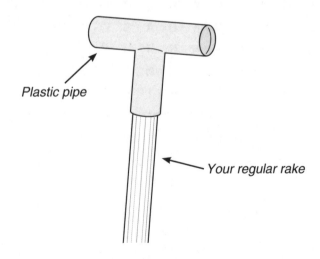

*Plastic pipe*

*Your regular rake*

# DAD JOKES

*INTERVIEWER: DESCRIBE
YOURSELF IN THREE WORDS.
INTERVIEWEE: NOT GOOD AT MATHS.*

---

*WHY DOES A FLAMINGO
STAND ON ONE LEG?
IF IT DIDN'T STAND
ON ANY, IT'D FALL OVER.*

---

*OUR WEDDING WAS SO BEAUTIFUL,
EVEN THE CAKE WAS IN TIERS.*

# INACCURATE NAMES

Are you a pedantic dad that reels in horror at inaccuracy? If so, you'll cringe at this bunch of misleading facts!

1. **Ninety Mile Beach on the western coast of Northland, New Zealand, is actually 88 kilometres (55 miles) in length. It's still a beach, though!**

2. **The highly venomous African black mamba snake is actually grey or greyish-brown.**

3. **Turkish baths originated in Rome.**

4. **A guinea pig is not a type of pig, and a prairie dog is not a dog – they are both rodents.**

5. **Peanuts are legumes – not nuts.**

6. **A shooting star is not a star but a meteor or meteoroid, whose definition is "a solid object moving in interplanetary space, of a size considerably smaller than an asteroid and considerably larger than an atom".**

7. **Pont Neuf in Paris is the city's oldest bridge – its name means "new bridge".**

8. **The Thousand Islands archipelago on the Canada–US border comprises closer to two thousand islands – 1,864 to be precise.**

# ANIMAL–RELATED MUSIC

Let this evening's playlist be inspired by the artists below – if you can get the questions right, of course. There's sure to be a type of music to suit every dad's taste.

1. Which girl group was formed in 1998, consisting of Liz, Kerry and Heidi?

2. Which rapper was born Calvin Broadus in 1971?

3. "Hotel California" is often regarded as the most famous song by which band?

4. Which band released the well-known song "Born To Be Wild" in 1968?

5. Which singer had hits with "Kiss from a Rose" and "Crazy" in the 1990s?

6. Who had a 1983 hit with "All Night Long (All Night)"?

7. Nicole Scherzinger is associated with which girl group?

8. The one-armed musician Rick Allen is best known as the drummer of which band?

# CROSSWORD

Film-loving dads will speed through this crossword puzzle, as the answers are all names of well-known movies. Are you up to it? Lights, camera… action!

1. **Leave the room – now! (3, 3)**

2. **Combat organization (5, 4)**

3. **Terminate William (4, 4)**

4. **A fantasy dreamworld (2, 2, 4)**

5. **Vehicle jam (7)**

6. **Naughty St Nicholas (3, 5)**

7. **Angry male bovine (6, 4)**

8. **To yell (6)**

9. **Type of dizziness (7)**

# NEGATIVELY SPEAKING, ARE YOU POSITIVE?

TV remote controls, children's toys, clocks… They all need batteries, but how do you tell if those small cylinders of power have lost their punch? You can't exactly open them up, can you?

It's all in the bounce! Take a battery and drop it onto a hard surface – negative side down – from a 2.5–5 centimetre (1–2 inch) height. If the battery is a dud, it will perform a cheeky little bounce; if it's still got some life in it, you'll simply hear a small thud.

And why does this happen, might you ask? A "working" battery still contains a gel-like substance that absorbs any bounce, whereas the inside of a battery that needs binning has turned solid – hence, the "bounce ability". Life is full of small wonders, eh?

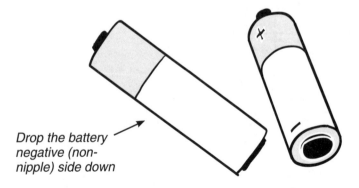

*Drop the battery negative (non-nipple) side down*

## ?

# TRUE OR FALSE?

Test yourself with this set of tricky true-or-false questions.
Bank the ones you guessed incorrectly and use them to
dazzle your friends!

1. **The entertainer Rod Hull died while adjusting his TV aerial.**

2. **The Great Wall of China is longer than the distance from London to Beijing.**

3. **Peter Shilton won more than 125 caps for the England national football team.**

4. **Michael Keaton's real name is Michael Douglas.**

5. **The Mariana Trench is deeper than Mt Everest is high.**

6. **Dolly Parton is Taylor Swift's godmother.**

7. **The first sauce produced by Heinz was tomato ketchup.**

8. **A "jiffy" is an actual unit of time.**

# DAD JOKES

*WHAT DO YOU CALL
A DEER WITH NO EYES?
NO IDEA.*

---

*WHAT DO YOU CALL A DEER
WITH NO EYES AND NO LEGS?
STILL NO IDEA!*

---

*WHAT DOES AN ANGRY PEPPER DO?
IT GETS JALAPEÑO FACE.*

---

*TIME FLIES LIKE AN ARROW BUT
FRUIT FLIES LIKE A BANANA.*

# THE "ULTIMATE SPY" TRIVIA

What do an American bird expert and the most famous fictional spy have in common? It's a boring question... or is it?

OK, let's not keep you in suspense for too long. They have the same name: James Bond.

In fact, the creator of the Bond novels took the name of his hero from the author of *Birds of the West Indies* – a certain James Bond. Mr Bond (the ornithologist) was born in 1900 in Pennsylvania, and his book caught the eye of Ian Fleming, who was a keen birdwatcher living in Jamaica.

Fleming wanted the name of his main character to be "the simplest, dullest, plainest-sounding name" he could find. He later added, "I wanted to find a name which wouldn't have any sort of romantic overtones, like Peregrine Carruthers."

Well, Mr Fleming, you certainly picked a good name for a literary character that would later star in more than 24 official films.

Dads, if you take anything from this piece of trivia, it should be this: sometimes the most ordinary formula works the best!

# IN THE SNICK OF TIME

Shaving – dads either loathe it or love it. Whether you adore or despise this fundamental grooming routine, chances are you'll have cut yourself at least once – and if you haven't, Lady Luck must be constantly smiling on you!

When you see blood due to a razor nick, don't be tempted to dab the slash with tissue. Instead, petroleum jelly is a much more effective way of keeping the blood at bay. Apply a smidgen of this stuff to the shaving mishap and you'll be as good as new in no time. As it contains waxes and mineral oils, it forms a water-protective barrier that no tissue can muster. Plus, you'll look like a professional boxer!

*A dab will do!*

*Do not use in place of petrol or jelly*

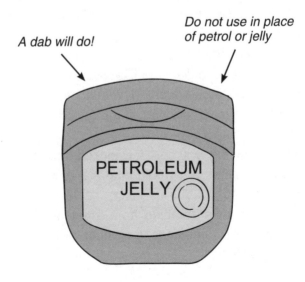

PETROLEUM JELLY

# LETTERBOX

Cross out all the letters below that appear more than once. The remaining ones will then spell out a word – what is it?

| | | | | |
|---|---|---|---|---|
| U | W | M | X | C |
| S | D | B | R | I |
| F | Z | O | D | N |
| I | X | C | R | T |
| Z | E | M | S | W |
| A | F | N | O | Y |

# FOOD JIG

The names of five delicious foods have been conveniently sliced into sections. Simply join the pieces together to find out what they are. Each letter slice can only be used once!

SCO

PO

HO

ME

NE

RK

T

ATB

SAN

P

DWI

AL

D

IE

OG

LS

CH

# DOWN WITH THE KIDS

Ever had a conversation with your son or daughter (or anyone under the age of 16), only to be mystified by their language? What is a "Finsta", for instance? Here are some buzzwords you probably didn't use in your day and that should be useful to all dads. Keep slaying, and you'll be a GOAT in no time.

**GOAT** – "greatest of all time"

**Finsta** – a second Instagram account, often clandestine or secret

**Flex** – to show off

**Slay** – to do something well or to look good

**Curve** – to reject someone's (romantic) advances

**Tea** – gossip, news, a story, etc.

**No cap** – true, not fake, no lie, etc.

**Throw shade** – to give someone a dirty look

**Beat** – to apply make-up aggressively with often comic effects

**Clout** – fame, importance, influence, etc.

**Gucci** – good

**OK Boomer** – dismissing someone who is behaving or talking in a way that's old-fashioned

## ?

# WE ASKED 100 PEOPLE...

The questions below were asked to 100 people. Can you guess what the three top answers were for each one?

1. **Name a starter that's often on the menu in a restaurant.**

2. **Name something that people spray on themselves.**

3. **Name a Christmas carol or song that you might hear at a school nativity play.**

4. **Name a musical instrument you blow.**

5. **Name something you'd do to let a guest know it's time for them to leave.**

# ICE-LOLLY CONUNDRUM

Are you a dad with young 'uns? Fed up with ice cream or lollies melting from the cone or stick, ending up on their clothes and hands?

Fret no more! To solve this ice-cold conundrum, find a small plastic lid (cake cases or inverted takeaway coffee cups are ideal) and cut a hole in its centre. Insert the dessert-laden cone or ice-lolly stick through the gap, and you have a perfect "drip tray". This works particularly well on holidays or during the summer months. Ta-da!

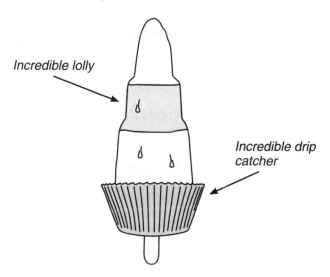

Incredible lolly

Incredible drip catcher

# WORD SEARCH

Alright, Dave? Find all the surnames of famous Davids or Daves – your name might even be in this one!

**Tennant**

**Duchovny**

**Bowie**

**Fincher**

**Hasselhoff**

**Cassidy**

**Lynch**

**Beckham**

**Grohl**

**Copperfield**

**Letterman**

**Blaine**

**Schwimmer**

**Gower**

**Seaman**

```
J F L X S E T F C V B G H G U
J I A Y D S C H W I M M E R B
D N R F N H K L M N J P M O T
U C D L A C S A A X C A T H C
C H J K E B H D S W H T U L O
H E J T N T V C F K H F D S P
O R M E H B T G C Y I F R E P
V C X N G H J E I B L A I N E
N N B N Y T B D R S G U H B R
Y S E A M A N D A M Z X R T F
V B H N I A N M A J A Y H E I
T G F T J U Y G F T R N I R E
V C A S S I D Y G T R W D F L
D D A H A S S E L H O F F T D
G O W E R R A E W B T R E U P
```

169

# DAD JOKE

A MAN WALKS INTO A BAR AND ASKS FOR TEN PINTS OF BEER. THE BARMAN POURS THE DRINKS AND SETS THEM ON THE BAR. THE MAN DRINKS THE FIRST PINT, THEN THE THIRD, THE FIFTH, THE SEVENTH AND THEN THE NINTH, LEAVING THE REST. THE CONFUSED BARMAN ASKS THE MAN WHY HE LEFT THE OTHERS. "OH," SAID THE MAN. "I JUST LIKE THE ODD PINT."

# MISSING LETTER

Every now and then, dads get the urge to break a sweat and shed a bit of weight. Each of the following words is missing a letter. Put them all into the grid below to reveal an item seen at the gym!

1 _EARD

2 HE_RD

3 _AMBLE

4 SLUM_ER

5 SW_AT

6 ROL_ER

7 C_AIM

| 1 | 2 | 3 | 4 | 5 | 6 | 7 |
|---|---|---|---|---|---|---|
|   |   |   |   |   |   |   |

# DAD JOKES

*A HAMBURGER WALKS INTO A BAR. THE BARMAN SAYS, "I'M SORRY, WE DON'T SERVE FOOD HERE."*

---

*A JUKEBOX WALKS INTO A BAR. THE BARMAN SAYS, "I CAN'T SERVE YOU – LAST NIGHT YOU WERE OUT OF ORDER."*

---

*THE FUTURE, THE PRESENT AND THE PAST WALKED INTO A BAR. THINGS GOT A LITTLE TENSE.*

# TEACH CHILDREN HOW TO CLEAN

This life hack could be a game-changer for dads across the globe! If you think teaching children the value of a little hard work is good and cleaning is bad, then merge the two to your advantage!

Let's take a scenario: you're cooking a delicious chicken risotto, but your clumsy mitts have failed to keep all the rice in the pan – some wayward grains have gone on the floor. Do you reach for a dustpan and brush? No! Instead, drop a cut-out cardboard square template on the floor, and challenge your children to brush all the grains into it within 30 seconds. It'll be a fun game for them, and dads will get out of doing the chore. Brilliant, huh?

Unsuspecting child

Clean floor

# DINGBATS

Use your creative imagination to work out this fiendish dingbat. You can do it – you're a dad!

## HAND HAND HAND HAND

# DECK

# HOW MANY WORDS?

Make as many words (four letters minimum) as you can, each including the central letter highlighted. There's also a wonderful nine-letter word – but what is it?

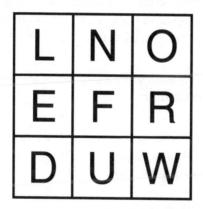

# USELESS TRIVIA

Is there such a thing as "useless" trivia? After all, it can earn you intellectual brownie points from family and friends – and which dad doesn't want these? Also, it can win you the top prize in a quiz! Here's a selection of random trivia that could be far from "useless".

1. The dish French toast is older than France.

2. Cheese is the most shoplifted food item in the world – estimated as 230 million kilograms (508 million pounds) of the stuff stolen annually… That's the weight of around 127,000 cars!

3. Iceland has approximately 22 puffins for every human inhabitant.

4. In North Carolina, there is a law firm called Eggers, Eggers, Eggers & Eggers – shortened, wisely, to Eggers Law.

5. American chef Ruth Wakefield invented the chocolate-chip cookie in the 1930s. She sold the idea to Nestlé for a lifetime supply of chocolate.

6. The famous "old book smell" is officially described as "grass and vanilla".

# DAD JOKES

**WHAT DO YOU CALL
A FISH WITH NO EYES?
A "FSH".**

---

**WHY DO BEES HAVE STICKY HAIR?
BECAUSE THEY USE HONEYCOMBS.**

---

**A LIZARD WENT TO THE DOCTOR
COMPLAINING ABOUT HIS SEX LIFE.
HE WAS DIAGNOSED WITH
EREPTILE DYSFUNCTION.**

# SPORTING NICKNAMES

Seeing how dads love a good nickname (and sport), here is another quiz of sporting nicknames to have a go at. Simply name the sportsperson from the nicknames provided.

1. **"The Baby-faced Assassin" (football)**

2. **"Flo-Jo" (athletics)**

3. **"The Black Knight" (golf)**

4. **The four batsmen who were collectively nicknamed "The Fab Four" in India in the late 1990s and early 2000s**

5. **"Judith" (rugby union)**

6. **"The King of Clay" (tennis)**

7. **"The White Pelé" (football)**

8. **"The Ace in the Pack" (snooker)**

9. **"Jackpot" (darts)**

10. **"Hitman" (WWF wrestler)**

# ODD-ONE-OUT ANAGRAM

Which of the following five sport-related anagrams is the odd one out? Get going, dads!

1 **WOLYEL**

2 **RUPPEL**

3 **NEGER**

4 **LUBE**

5 **KINP**

# WORD LADDER

If you enjoy angling, this should be easy. Change one letter at a time to get to a four-letter fish.

**DARE**

**CARP**

# SPORT JIG

The names of four sports have been cut up into small sections. Simply join the segments together to reveal them.

CR

TA

SU

AR

OQ

BLE

MO

CHE

UET

TE

WRE

RY

NN

STL

ING

IS

# SECRET GOODIES

Goodies aren't just for children, or something you give to your better half to say "thank you" or "sorry"! Yes, dads are also allowed a tasty chocolate treat without sharing.

But when the "secret" drawer has been discovered, you could run out of suitable places to hide illicit confectionery. Sure, you could place snacks under chairs or beds, but often you'll forget their whereabouts, so by the time you've remembered, they'll be in poor shape.

So commit to memory one secure place – think of something that no one else likes. For instance, if you're the only family member who eats porridge, conceal your treats inside its packaging for a foolproof hiding place. You'll then be able to enjoy the success of your wiliness, while your family will be none the wiser.

Secret stash

Dad's boring oats

# DINGBAT

This will try even the cleverest dads. What could this dingbat possibly mean? Stop scratching your head and get to it!

# SUR*BM*WANCE

# ALCOHOL TRIVIA

While enjoying your favourite tipple, consider these interesting facts about the wonderful world of alcohol.

1. The largest number of varieties of beer available on tap is 369, achieved by The Raleigh Beer Garden in the US. Due to the scale of their ever-changing selection, the premises do not print a paper menu!

2. The largest margarita was 32,176 litres (8,500 US gallons)!

3. The most people officially recorded on a pub crawl is 4,885!

4. A Harvey Wallbanger cocktail is named after US surfer Tom Harvey. Legend has it that he asked for the drink (essentially a screwdriver with added herbal liqueur), and kept banging his surfboard and running into walls after imbibing a few of these strong tipples.

5. Do you prefer beer to margaritas? It seems American citizens enjoy both, as there are 185,000 margaritas consumed per hour in the US.

6. Austrian Leo Pisker has collected nearly 153,000 different beer mats. Now, perhaps that's a record some dads could feasibly break!

# TRUE OR FALSE?

Work out which of the statements below are true and which are false. Sounds easy, right? Wrong!

1. **A tequila sunrise cocktail contains tequila.**

2. **Mexico is south of the Equator.**

3. **Meghan Markle's real first name is Rachel.**

4. **The bishop, king and queen are the only chess pieces that can move diagonally.**

5. **The Seychelles has only one Burger King outlet, but no McDonald's.**

6. **There are more countries in Asia than in Africa.**

7. **The first Christmas song to be broadcast from space was "Silent Night".**

8. **Blur's original name was Seymour.**

9. **The can opener was invented before the tin can.**

10. **Richard Dunne, Patrick Vieira and Duncan Ferguson were sent off the same number of times in the English Premier League.**

**?**

# CLUED-UP

All the answers to these clues have a link – what's the connection?

1 **Female US tennis player who won 12 singles Grand Slam titles**

2 **Potent pain reliever named after a Greek god**

3 **Traditional colour of chess pieces**

# DAD JOKE

A YOUNG OUTLAW WALKED INTO A TOWN IN THE WILD WEST. HE WORE A BROWN PAPER HAT, BROWN PAPER TROUSERS, BROWN PAPER SHIRT AND BROWN PAPER BOOTS. THE SHERIFF ASKED THE COCKY UPSTART HIS NAME. "WHY, I'M THE BROWN PAPER KID," THE OUTLAW SAID. "YOU MUST HAVE HEARD OF ME — I'M NOTORIOUS IN THESE PARTS." THE SHERIFF SHOOK HIS HEAD. "NOPE, I NEVER HEARD OF YOU, BROWN PAPER KID. WHAT HAVE YOU DONE TO MAKE YOU SO NOTORIOUS?" AND THE BROWN PAPER KID REPLIED, "WELL, I'VE DONE A FAIR BIT OF RUSTLING."

# WORD SEARCH

Hopefully, you'll be reading this outside in the sun, so what better subject for a word search than scrumptious foods you may find at a barbecue?

**Lamb chop**

**Burger**

**Sausage**

**Salmon**

**Shrimp**

**Hot dog**

**Ketchup**

**Mustard**

**Kebab**

**Chicken leg**

**Coleslaw**

**Potato salad**

```
J  M  N  B  A  M  U  S  T  A  R  D  Q  R  Y
B  W  A  C  O  L  E  S  L  A  W  A  C  V  A
C  U  J  Y  G  F  D  S  A  Q  W  R  T  C  L
S  K  R  L  J  N  B  G  H  Y  T  D  K  L  A
A  V  E  G  E  T  U  G  S  S  G  I  G  H  M
U  K  C  V  E  Y  M  N  A  E  J  O  H  F  B
S  E  E  R  A  R  Y  G  L  F  D  B  H  N  C
A  T  T  E  W  S  A  N  M  T  K  I  Y  G  H
G  C  Y  P  K  M  E  V  O  F  T  F  D  E  O
E  H  C  D  H  K  U  H  N  B  K  I  T  D  P
W  U  M  N  C  E  G  C  R  Y  X  B  V  F  T
R  P  S  I  X  B  B  Y  T  H  J  H  V  G  H
J  K  H  Y  T  A  V  C  F  S  H  R  I  M  P
G  C  C  X  E  B  S  S  F  G  J  K  K  N  B
K  P  L  P  O  T  A  T  O  S  A  L  A  D  A
```

# UTTERLY QUOTABLE

Can you work out the quote from a famous space opera? We won't tell you the number of words, but the letters are in the correct order!

| | A | | T | | E | F | | | C | | B | | W | I | | | | U |
|---|---|---|---|---|---|---|---|---|---|---|---|---|---|---|---|---|---|---|

# FOUR BY FOUR

If you're a dad with only a few minutes to spare, put your feet up briefly and solve this mini crossword. Try to complete it in just one minute!

| 1 | 2 | 3 | 4 |
|---|---|---|---|
| 5 |   |   |   |
| 6 |   |   |   |
| 7 |   |   |   |

**ACROSS**

**1** Decorative metal piece

**5** Sit (for)

**6** Eras

**7** Blemish

**DOWN**

**1** Unsolicited, irritating emails – edible?

**2** Roman gown

**3** Consumer

**4** Computer station/ office table

# MANLY DINGBAT

You may have had one, aspire to have one someday or have one already! What is it?

**GOGOGO**
**GO**
**GO**
**GO**
**GO**

# WOULD YOU BELIEVE IT?

If you love bizarre sporting scenarios, they don't come much stranger than the following incident from an amateur UK football match in 2005. Read on and decide which is the correct reasoning behind Andy Wain's notoriety.

Let's set the scene: Peterborough North End were up against Royal Mail AYL. In the sixty-third minute, Mr Wain saw red – literally – when he was sent off for aggressive behaviour. Why did this make the news?

a) **He was Peterborough North End's goalkeeper and broke the crossbar in anger.**

b) **He was Royal Mail AYL's manager and became irate after he was stuck in traffic.**

c) **He was a streaker and punched a player who tried to detain him.**

d) **He was the referee and sent himself off after an altercation with a player.**

# MAKESHIFT CAR CUP-HOLDER

Nowadays, most cars have the luxury of cup holders. But if dads are too "old-school" to believe in such immaterial devices, there is a remarkably simple solution, should the need arise.

Place a solid shoe or low-heeled boot on the passenger-side floor. Place your drink – be it a soft-drink can, water bottle or hot-beverage cup – in the shoe for a solid receptacle.

If Nancy Sinatra had known about this little gem, perhaps she would have sung "These Boots are Made for Holding Drinks in Cars". Not as catchy as her original song, to be fair!

Upright cup

Your shoe

# HOW BIZARRE!

Are you a dad with a love of unusual trivia? You've come to the right place! How about these little gems to raise your eyebrows?

1. J. Fred Muggs was born in French Cameroon in 1952 and was soon in the spotlight when he starred as co-host for NBC's *Today Show* in the mid-1950s. He officially retired in the 1970s, seemingly having had his fill of show business. Not that weird, right? Well, Mr Muggs was a chimpanzee!

2. During the famous Oktoberfest in Germany, no one is considered to be legally drunk. Go for it!

3. It is against the law to urinate in a canal in the Netherlands, unless you're pregnant (which, if you're reading this book, is fairly unlikely!).

4. A number of deaths in the Philippines have become known as the "My Way" killings, because they have been perpetrated in karaoke bars by customers who just couldn't stand listening to the song one more time. Maybe just stick to "Bohemian Rhapsody", even if you usually "murder" the song!

# WORD LADDER

Here's a word ladder for film enthusiasts. Change one letter at a time to get to a four-letter film of the 1990s. We hope it's not too hot to handle!

SOUR

_____

_____

_____

_____

HEAT

# ODD-ONE-OUT ANAGRAM

Take a walk on the wild side! These anagrams are all animals – but can you spot the odd one out?

1. MUE

2. LAWYABL

3. DOING

4. CAKJAL

5. TAMBOW

# PERSONAL HOLIDAY SAFETY

Beaches are notorious for pickpockets and thieves. Shame on them! So, stay one step ahead of unsavoury opportunists with this brilliant suggestion. Take a sunscreen container and empty the gooey contents (or use first, then rinse the insides!). You now have a clean, empty bottle.

OK, so now what? Simply use the container to store keys, money – even mobile phones. No one is ever going to steal an innocuous ointment bottle. Well, you'd hope not, anyway…

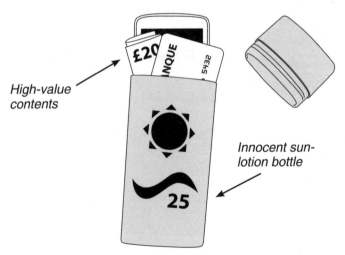

*High-value contents*

*Innocent sun-lotion bottle*

# THE FILM CRITIC'S GREATEST FILMS

Call yourself a film buff? Roger Ebert was the film buff's buff – the buffiest of all film critics. The US moviegoer became the film critic of the *Chicago Sun-Times* in 1967 and went on to review thousands of flicks. Sadly, he passed away in 2013, but not before giving readers and viewers his list of greatest films. He was quoted as saying, "One of the gifts one movie lover can give another is the title of a wonderful film they have not yet discovered."

Here is a selection of his "four-star maximum rating" movies.

*Nosferatu* – 1922

*Metropolis* – 1927

*Stagecoach* – 1939

*Shadow of a Doubt* – 1943

*Cool Hand Luke* – 1967

*Small Change* – 1976

*Platoon* – 1986

*Leaving Las Vegas* – 1995

*The Hurt Locker* – 2008

How many of these have you seen, and do you agree with Mr Ebert?

# WORD SEARCH

The referee has blown their whistle, so you've now got just 100 seconds to find the ten sports below. No cheating or you'll be banned!

**Cricket**

**Hockey**

**Rugby**

**Horse racing**

**Boxing**

**Speedway**

**Badminton**

**Tennis**

**Squash**

**Baseball**

```
F D H O C K E Y A M N H G H Y
U O P L C R I C K E T O F B V
G F D S D T B V B J U R A A N
B T Y T F D X S E N F S A S B
N U E T G F H K O N K E O E G
F B Y N Y T R T G H B R A B J
J A G F N C N D E R T A G A Y
S K I U J I G A K N G C A L R
Q D C G M C S T Y B I I K L H
U N J D G U J O K J H N D S W
A Z A A C A A N M R U G B Y C
S B X H J U Y T R W Y I J G F
H V B N H T W O E Y F S A W A
K H A K O I Y S P E E D W A Y
S B O X I N G K J H I U A U Y
```

# DAD JOKES

DON'T SPELL "PART" BACKWARDS.
IT'S A TRAP.

---

WHAT'S ORANGE AND
SOUNDS LIKE A PARROT?
A CARROT.

---

WHAT'S THE DIFFERENCE
BETWEEN A HIPPO AND A ZIPPO?
ONE IS VERY HEAVY; THE OTHER
IS A LITTLE LIGHTER.

# ❓

# WHAT OR WHO AM I?

Below are five brief statements – work out who "I" is in each one.

1. I was completed on 11 April 1931, and I have 102 floors.

2. I was a 94-year-old English actor and one of my notable roles was in the third Bond film.

3. I was opened in 1937 and my longest span is 1,280 metres (4,200 feet).

4. I was first shown on English TV on 11 September 1972 – and I'm still going.

5. In a game of this sport, I'm one of six – and I'm 71 centimetres (28 inches) in height.

# DINGBAT

All dads know that women are always right! So, what is the meaning of this dingbat?

| MR | MRS |
|----|-----|
| HIM | HER |
| SIR | LADY |
| HE | SHE |
| MICHAEL | MICHAELA |

# CROSS OUT

Cross out the letters in the grid below that appear more than once. With the remaining ones, find the item that is useful to dads on a camping or walking expedition! (Hint: Some of the remaining letters may need to be used more than once!)

| H | E | J | W | K |
|---|---|---|---|---|
| X | R | B | T | J |
| N | I | E | Q | S |
| W | U | H | V | D |
| X | N | B | T | V |
| A | I | C | Q | D |

# UNLOCKING
# MISTAKEN IDENTITY

Dads have a lot of keys. Garage, car, house, office…
The list is endless. So they'd be forgiven for not instantly
recognizing which one they're looking for, since they all
appear so similar. But it's infuriating searching for the
correct one, right?

Simply colour-coordinate each key by applying nail
polish – something like "green for garage", "crimson for
car", etc. Once your brain memorizes the colours, you'll
select the right key first time, every time!

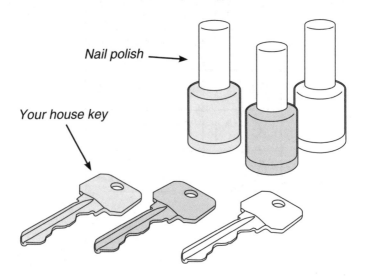

Nail polish

Your house key

# DAD JOKES

**DID YOU HEAR THE
ONE ABOUT A WINDOW?
YOU'D SEE RIGHT THROUGH IT.**

---

**DID YOU HEAR THE ONE ABOUT A WALL?
YOU'D NEVER GET OVER IT.**

---

**DID YOU HEAR THE ONE ABOUT A BIN?
IT'S RUBBISH.**

# PERSON OF THE YEAR

No, it's not you (yet!). A lot of dads will aspire to be one of *Time* magazine's Person of the Year, like the person mentioned below. All their letters are in sequence, but several have been omitted. Who is it?

| M | | K | U | | E | B | R | |
|---|---|---|---|---|---|---|---|---|

# HOWZAT FOR A SPORTY PUZZLE?

Starting with the letter in bold and moving one letter at a time, either vertically or horizontally, find four terms associated with cricket. The last letter of each word is the first letter of the next.

| A | T | O | I | M | N | O |
|---|---|---|---|---|---|---|
| S | H | C | F | H | I | D |
| E | E | O | U | T | R | E |
| E | S | F | O | X | D | U |
| A | D | U | N | B | E | M |
| M | E | R | P | X | I | P |
| I | S | C | O | A | R | E |

# TAKE FIVE

There are only three answers to this mini crossword, but four clues – one is a red herring! Fit each correct answer twice into the grid below, once going across and once going down.

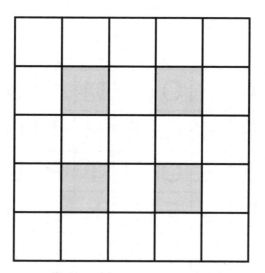

**CLUE 1: Church singers**
**CLUE 2: River mammal**
**CLUE 3: Asian country**
**CLUE 4: Relating to the countryside**

# HOW MANY WORDS?

This puzzle could go on forever! Simply write down as many words as you can (four letters minimum), each including the central letter highlighted. There's also a nine-letter word for those clever enough to spot it. What is it?

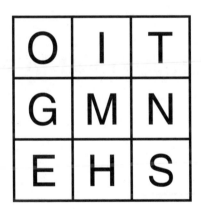

| O | I | T |
|---|---|---|
| G | M | N |
| E | H | S |

# FILM DINGBAT

Dads – what on earth is this 1942 film? You've got more than enough hints to work this out!

## 1600 PENNSYLVANIA AVE NW

# LINKWORD

Find the missing link between these words. The first and second word of each set go together, as do the second and third. Get to it, dads!

1 **PUTTING _ _ _ _ _ SLEEVES**

2 **BLUE _ _ _ _ _ RED**

3 **BLACK _ _ _ _ POT**

4 **SNOOKER _ _ _ _ _ SERVICE**

5 **GOAL _ _ _ _ MAN**

# TRIPLE TOWERS

This is a short quiz, on many levels – as the questions are all about famous landmark buildings!

**1** Sears Tower is a landmark building in a large US city, whose name was changed in 2009. Do you know the new name, and the city?

**2** Standing at 328 metres (1,076 feet) in height and completed in 1997, the Sky Tower is the tallest building in which southern-hemisphere city?

**3** Which famous towers prominently featured in the 1999 film *Entrapment*, which starred Sean Connery and Catherine Zeta-Jones?

**4** The Transamerica Pyramid is a distinctive building in which US city?

**5** In which city is the towering Burj Khalifa located?

# GRILLED FACTS

Dads and barbecues go together like hot dogs and mustard. Next time you're in charge of the grill, delight your ravenous guests with these facts!

1. The longest barbecue recorded was created in the Philippines. It measured 8,000 metres (26,247 feet) in length! If it had been upended, it would have been higher than the fifteenth-highest mountain. A total of 6,000 bags of charcoal were used – now, that's a lot of sausages!

2. The word "barbecue" was first used (as a noun) in 1697 by British buccaneer William Dampier.

3. The largest barbecue attendance was 45,252 people. Must have been a pretty big garden…

4. In 2020, 23,456 servings of barbecued beef were served in eight hours in Brazil. This required 140 barbecuers!

5. In the US, the most common barbecuing utensils are, in order: long-handled tongs, forks, long-handled spatulas and grill-cleaning brushes. So, now you know!

6. George Washington's diaries detailed barbecues, including a mammoth one that lasted three days!

# ODD-ONE-OUT
# ANAGRAM

Unscramble the words to discover the names of various sportsmen. But which one is the anomaly?

1 **CONATAN**

2 **MEYRAN**

3 **DINIMAL**

4 **RADIVOL**

5 **MAPSARS**

# SUDOKU

Fill in the rows with numbers from one to nine, but remember: each row, each column and each of the nine 3x3 squares must all contain the digits with no repeats.

| | 6 | | | 2 | 5 | | | 9 |
|---|---|---|---|---|---|---|---|---|
| | | | | | | | | 4 |
| | | | 7 | | 4 | 5 | 2 | |
| 9 | 4 | | | | | | | |
| | | | | | 6 | | 5 | |
| | 5 | | 4 | 3 | | | | 8 |
| | 7 | | 5 | | 9 | | 3 | 2 |
| 6 | | | | | 3 | 1 | | |
| | | 2 | | | | 6 | | |

# FOOTIE WORD-PATH

The grid below contains the surnames of four famous football personalities (past or present). Start with the letter in bold and move one letter at a time, either vertically or horizontally, to find the quartet. The last letter of each word is the first letter of the next.

| B | E | K | O | P | I | C |
|---|---|---|---|---|---|---|
| A | C | K | H | O | P | B |
| R | S | R | A | R | A | D |
| T | T | Y | M | A | U | O |
| F | N | E | K | T | J | N |
| Y | P | W | O | W | G | A |
| G | H | P | R | E | U | P |

# CHEEKY LITTLE GRID

First, solve the clues, from one to five. Then, rearrange the letters in the shaded squares to discover a country.

1. **Brothers Grimm character (breadcrumbs)**

2. **Victoria cake**

3. **German capital city**

4. **Former Ivory Coast footballer**

5. **Lady – Anglo-Saxon exhibitionist**

| 1 | | | | | |
|---|---|---|---|---|---|
| 2 | | | | | |
| 3 | | | | | |
| 4 | | | | | |
| 5 | | | | | |

**?**

# MULTIPLE ANSWERS

You should get *at least* one correct answer from the following trio of brain-teasers. If you achieve a full house on any question, award yourself the title of "Dad Genius"!

**1** **According to the International Bartenders Association for cocktails, name the eight ingredients that comprise a Long Island iced tea (garnish and ice cubes not included).**

**2** **Name the first eight albums released by The Beatles.**

**3** **Name the 14 US states on the East Coast.**

# DAD JOKES

*A HUSBAND WENT ON A TRAMPOLINE FOR THE FIRST TIME. "HOW WAS IT?" ASKED HIS WIFE. HE SHRUGGED: "UP AND DOWN."*

---

*A SHIP CARRYING RED PAINT COLLIDED WITH A SHIP CARRYING BROWN PAINT. THE CREWS WERE MAROONED.*

---

*BREAKING NEWS! A MAN DROWNED IN A BOWL OF MUESLI. IT WAS A STRONG CURRANT.*

# MYSTERY TV TRACK

Attention, goggle-box dads! The name of a TV series has been entered into the grid below. Start with the letter in bold, then move either vertically or horizontally to discover the title. Good luck

| S | O | D | A | B | G |
|---|---|---|---|---|---|
| T | **B** | I | W | G | A |
| U | R | E | Y | N | U |
| N | F | A | K | I | U |
| O | M | L | C | J | A |

# JIG JIG!

I bet you look good on the dance floor! The names of four dances have been cut into sections. Join the pieces to piece them back together.

QU

T

JI

AME

IC

AN

TT

RIC

KST

GO

ERB

AN

EP

OTH

UG

SMO

# CANDLELIT DINNER
# A-OK

Does lighting hard-to-reach candles really annoy you? Sometimes, standard matches are just too short to ignite the flames. The same with cigarette lighters. Time to use longer matches… unless, you've run out of them. What now?

Light a stick of dried spaghetti to minimize burning yourself. It has to be *dried* spaghetti, though. (What would your family think if you used cooked pasta?) And it has to be spaghetti for this simple life hack – no penne pasta or any other shape!

NB this tip will usually only be feasible at home – unless you have the urge to carry dried spaghetti around with you!

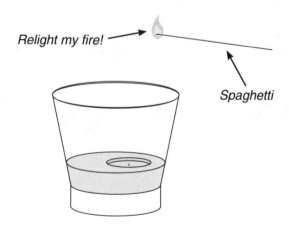

*Relight my fire!*

*Spaghetti*

# PLEASE SEND YOUR CV...

Bored of your nine-to-five and looking for something a little bit different? Here are some actual jobs (past and present) that some dads might find interesting – or politely decline!

**Sniffer** – the successful candidate would test the effectiveness of foot and underarm deodorants by sniffing people's body parts.

**Bottom bleacher** – not as horrible as it sounds: the job requires applying bleach to the bottom of leather shoes to lighten the colour of the outsoles.

**Chick sexer** – determining the sex of chicks is clearly skilled work, as there were university degrees offered in Japan to hone this precise skill.

**Ant catcher** – the worker digs up live ants for use in plastic ant farms; chubby-fingered dads need not apply!

**Egg smeller** – workers smell eggs after they are broken to check for spoilage. (If they are fine, at least they can have an omelette for their lunch!)

# CAMOUFLAGED CLUE

There is a species of animal below – with some letters omitted. All the ones that are there are in the correct order, though. We'll give you a "little" clue to the animal's identity: it's a little clue!

| | | G | | Y | | I | | P | | | O | | M | | |
|---|---|---|---|---|---|---|---|---|---|---|---|---|---|---|---|

# REALLY WILD LIST

It's cool to look out for the planet and all the creatures that call it home, so can you name the ten land mammals that can be adopted via the World Wildlife Fund website?

1 _____

2 _____

3 _____

4 _____

5 _____

6 _____

7 _____

8 _____

9 _____

10 _____

# DAD JOKE

MORE BREAKING NEWS! A LOCAL MAN IS SET TO DIVORCE HIS WIFE AFTER SHE SMEARED GLUE ON HIS COLLECTION OF FIREARMS. HE SAID, "SHE DENIED IT, OF COURSE, BUT I'M STICKING TO MY GUNS."

---

WHY DID THE CAN CRUSHER QUIT HIS JOB? BECAUSE IT WAS SODA-PRESSING.

---

WHAT LIES AT THE BOTTOM OF THE OCEAN AND TWITCHES? A NERVOUS WRECK.

# DINGBAT

Dads – can you work out this sneaky dingbat? Fair play if you can!

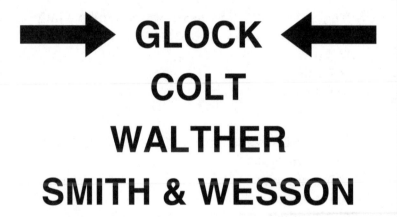

GLOCK
COLT
WALTHER
SMITH & WESSON

# WHO SAID THAT?

Dads have a habit of remembering quotes, so as to regale their friends with them in bars across the land. Below are some things said by famous figures. Simply choose the correct option to complete the quotes. Good luck!

1. **Napoleon Hill: "It takes half your life before you discover that life is a... "**
   a) Waste of time
   b) Do-it-yourself project
   c) Breeze

2. **Meghan Markle: "I've never wanted to be a lady who lunches – I've always wanted to be a woman who... "**
   a) Rules
   b) Dines
   c) Works

3. **Winston Churchill: "... is a little thing that makes a big difference."**
   a) Intelligence
   b) Courage
   c) Attitude

4. **Hans Christian Andersen: "Life itself is the most wonderful... "**
   a) Remedy
   b) Fairy tale
   c) Pleasure

# DAD JOKES

*A MAN WAS ADDICTED TO THE HOKEY-COKEY, BUT HE TURNED HIMSELF AROUND, AND THAT'S WHAT IT'S ALL ABOUT.*

---

*A WIFE YELLED TO HER HUSBAND FROM UPSTAIRS, "DO YOU EVER GET A SHOOTING PAIN ACROSS YOUR BODY, LIKE SOMEONE'S GOT A VOODOO DOLL OF YOU AND THEY'RE STABBING IT?" THE HUSBAND REPLIED, "NO." THE WIFE YELLED BACK, "HOW ABOUT NOW?!"*

## LOST AND FOUND

Dads can be scatterbrained sometimes. We're all human! But have you ever lost any of the items below?

All of these have ended up in the Transport for London's lost-property office, handed in after being recovered on the UK capital's trains and buses. So, the next time you're commuting on a train and you misplace a folder or ticket, just be thankful you don't have to contact lost property and explain why your jar of bull's sperm went astray…

Full-size house carpet

Judge's wig

Two and a half hundredweight (approximately 115 kilograms/18 stone) of sultanas

Garden slide

Park bench

Jar of bull's sperm

Dead bats in a container

Vasectomy kit

Two human skulls in a bag

Theatrical coffin

Stuffed eagle

Divan bed

Prosthetic leg

Lawnmower

# OLYMPIC CLUE

Below is a sport included in the Olympic Games. All the letters are in the correct order, though a few of them have been omitted, and the number of words hasn't been specified. Who said this was going to be easy?

| | H | | T | | I | G | | N | | S | | I | | |

# RIDDLE ME THIS...

What is the answer to his head-scratcher? You'll have to have your brain switched on for this one.

**"Twelve faces have no ears, with 42 eyes that can't see. Which pair do I seek?"**

# DAD JOKES

**LAST NIGHT I WENT TO A COMEDY AND PHILOSOPHY CONVENTION. LAUGHED MORE THAN I THOUGHT.**

---

**WHY DID THE INVISIBLE MAN TURN DOWN THE JOB OFFER? HE COULDN'T SEE HIMSELF DOING IT.**

---

**I BOUGHT A DOG FROM MY LOCAL BLACKSMITH. WHEN I GOT IT HOME, IT MADE A BOLT FOR THE DOOR.**

# ANSWERS

**p.6**
Answer: Typewriter

**p.7**
1. Zookeeper, goalkeeper, beekeeper, 2. In-laws, new boss, the Queen,
3. Bicycle, yacht, run/walk,
4. Daffodil, crocus, tulip,
5. Incredible Hulk, Jolly Green Giant, Kermit the Frog

**p.8**

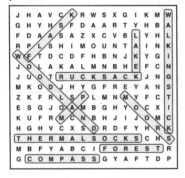

**p.11**
1. Spoiler, 2. Dash,
3. Suspension, 4. Boot,
5. Trunk
Answer: They are all parts of a car

**p.15**
1. *GoldenEye*, 2. Seven,
3. Emilio Largo, 4. *The Spy Who Loved Me*, 5. Britt Ekland, 6. Golf, 7. *A View to a Kill*, 8. Revenge

**p.17**
1. Kate Bush, 2. Lisa Stansfield, 3. Charlotte Church, 4. Alison Moyet,
5. Chrissie Hynde

**p.18**

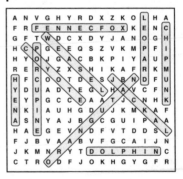

## p.20

1. Fish and chips,
2. Hawaiian pizza, 3. King prawn satay, 4. Special omelette, 5. Chicken tacos,
6. Lamb korma,
7. Cheeseburger, 8. Vindaloo

## p.22

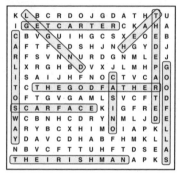

## p.24

1. b, 2. b, 3. a

## p.27

Answer: *Three Men in a Boat*

## p.30

One possible solution:
DOPE, NOPE, NONE, NINE, PINE, PINT

## p.32

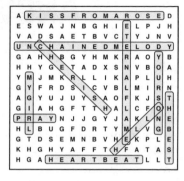

## p.34

| 1 | 2 | 3 | 4 | 5 | 6 | 7 |
|---|---|---|---|---|---|---|
| C | A | M | P | E | S | E |

## p.35

1. Ryan Giggs, 2. Cesc Fàbregas, 3. Wayne Rooney,
4. Frank Lampard, 5. Dennis Bergkamp, 6. David Silva,
7. Steven Gerrard, 8. David Beckham, 9. Teddy Sheringham,
10. Thierry Henry

**p.36**

| | | | |
|---|---|---|---|
| ¹D | ²R | ³A | ⁴W |
| ⁵E | A | S | E |
| ⁶E | V | I | L |
| ⁷R | E | A | D |

**p.38**

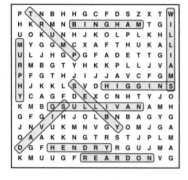

**p.41**

1. Ground, 2. Ball,
3. Take, 4. Top, 5. Sore

**p.42**

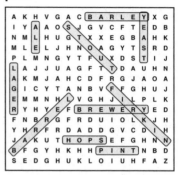

**p.45**

Answer: 3

**p.46**

1. Cravat, 2. Blazer,
3. Bomber jacket,
4. Pinstripe suit, 5. Flat cap

**p.47**

1. Tiger Woods, 2. Ernie Els,
3. Dustin Johnson,
4. Jordan Speith,
5. Francesco Molinari,
6. Henrik Stenson,
7. Brooks Koepka, 8. Bryson
DeChambeau, 9. Ian Poulter

**p.51**

Answer: b

**p.53**

Answer: *The Big Short*

**p.54**

Answer: Gopher

**p.56**

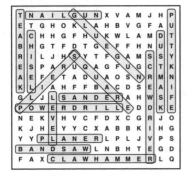

**p.60**

| S | P | A | I | N |
|---|---|---|---|---|
| P |   | D |   | E |
| A | D | D | E | R |
| I |   | E |   | V |
| N | E | R | V | E |

Red Herring: CLUE 1

**p.62**

1. Croquet, 2. Hockey,
3. Fencing, 4. Real tennis,
5. Badminton, 6. Cricket,
7. Handball, 8. Table tennis,
9. Polo, 10. Skydiving

**p.64**

1. Yellow, 2. Bison,
3. Ecuador, 4. Hare, 5. Beef,
6. Orange,
7. Fish, 8. Germany

**p.65**

Answer: Michael Jackson,
Madonna, Kiss, Duran Duran

**p.66**

Answer: The list is Roger
Moore Bond films in
chronological order. The next
in the sequence is *For Your
Eyes Only*.

**p.68**

1. Bruno Mars, 2. Meat Loaf,
3. Joe Cocker, 4. Usher,
5. Freddie Mercury, 6. Prince,
7. Muddy Waters, 8. Fats
Domino, 9. Tom Jones,
10. Sting, 11. Billy Ocean,
12. Chuck Berry

**p.72**

| 1 | 2 | 3 | 4 | 5 | 6 | 7 |
|---|---|---|---|---|---|---|
| S | E | A | T | T | L | E |

**p.73**

| 8 | 6 | 2 | 9 | 7 | 5 | 4 | 3 | 1 |
|---|---|---|---|---|---|---|---|---|
| 5 | 1 | 9 | 4 | 8 | 3 | 7 | 6 | 2 |
| 4 | 7 | 3 | 1 | 2 | 6 | 5 | 8 | 9 |
| 2 | 3 | 8 | 6 | 4 | 7 | 9 | 1 | 5 |
| 1 | 9 | 5 | 8 | 3 | 2 | 6 | 7 | 4 |
| 7 | 4 | 6 | 5 | 1 | 9 | 8 | 2 | 3 |
| 9 | 5 | 1 | 3 | 6 | 8 | 2 | 4 | 7 |
| 6 | 2 | 4 | 7 | 5 | 1 | 3 | 9 | 8 |
| 3 | 8 | 7 | 2 | 9 | 4 | 1 | 5 | 6 |

**p.78**

One possible solution:
SILL, SELL, FELL, FELT,
PELT, PELE

**p.79**

1. Delta, 2. Enzymes,
3. Firefox, 4. Gloria Gaynor,
5. Humphrey Bogart,
6. Idaho, 7. Jackie

**p.80**

1. Sprout, 2. Palmate,
3. Tuber, 4. Alpines,
5. Evergreen, 6. Bulb,
7. Seedling, 8. Runner,
9. Deadhead,
10. Hardy, 11 Stamen

**p.84**

1. Sleeper, 2. Half nelson,
3. Bear hug, 4. DDT
Answer: They are all holds/
manoeuvres in wrestling.

**p.86**

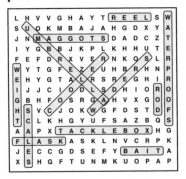

**p.89**

1. Four, 2. Six, 3. Three
(Aston Villa, Chelsea, Crystal
Palace), 4. One,
5. Two, 6. Nine, 7. Eight,
8. Ten, 9. Seven, 10. Five

**p.90**

| 1 | 2 | 4 | 3 | 5 | 9 | 7 | 8 | 6 |
|---|---|---|---|---|---|---|---|---|
| 7 | 6 | 9 | 1 | 8 | 4 | 5 | 2 | 3 |
| 8 | 5 | 3 | 2 | 7 | 6 | 9 | 1 | 4 |
| 3 | 9 | 6 | 4 | 1 | 5 | 2 | 7 | 8 |
| 2 | 4 | 7 | 9 | 3 | 8 | 6 | 5 | 1 |
| 5 | 8 | 1 | 6 | 2 | 7 | 4 | 3 | 9 |
| 9 | 3 | 8 | 5 | 4 | 2 | 1 | 6 | 7 |
| 6 | 1 | 2 | 7 | 9 | 3 | 8 | 4 | 5 |
| 4 | 7 | 5 | 8 | 6 | 1 | 3 | 9 | 2 |

**p.91**

Answer: Idaho, Oregon, New
York, Kentucky

**p.95**

Answer: Antwerp (1920). They are all Summer Olympics host cities

**p.96**

Answer: Hulk Hogan

**p.100**

Answer: Flashlight, tent, toilet paper, radio

**p.101**

Answer: Ale & Anaconda, Duff & Darts, Ankara & Pace, Rams & Mexico. The male name is 'Adam'.

**p.103:**

Answer: Adjustable wrench

**p.104**

1. Megan Fox, 2. *Million Dollar Baby*, 3. Carrie Fisher, 4. Marilyn Monroe, 5. Scarlett Johansson, 6. Emma Watson, 7. Sarah Jessica Parker, 8. Drew Barrymore

**p.105**

Answer: Tequila sunrise

**p.106**

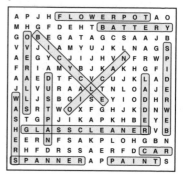

**p.110**

1. Clippers, 2. Straight razor, 3. Hairdryer, 4. Trimmers, 5. Pomade, 6. Gel

**p.112**

1. Allan Donald, 2. Andy Roddick, 3. James Wade, 4. William Perry, 5. Ernie Els, 6. Jason Leonard, 7. Roberto Baggio, 8. Alan McManus, 9. Martin Offiah, 10. Phil DeFreitas

**p.115**

One possible solution: COLD, TOLD, TOLL, POLL, POLE, HOLE

## p.116

1. Greece, 2. Japan,
3. Mexico, 4. Indonesia,
5. Jamaica, 6. Peru,
7. Russia/Ukraine, 8. Saudi
Arabia, 9. Spain, 10. Thailand
(well, pad thai would have
been too easy for you
foodies!)

## p.117

Answer: Referring,
amidships, nicknamed,
dartboard, odourless,
lamplight, paintwork,
hairstyle. Man's name =
Randolph

## p.118

1. Cello, 2. Ukulele,
3. Accordion, 4. Harmonica,
5. Tambourine, 6. Marimba,
7. Harpsichord, 8. Electric
guitar, 9. Oboe

## p.121

Answer: Ford, Damon,
Neeson, Nicholson

## p.122

| 4 | 1 | 3 | 6 | 2 | 5 | 9 | 7 | 8 |
|---|---|---|---|---|---|---|---|---|
| 5 | 7 | 2 | 3 | 9 | 8 | 1 | 6 | 4 |
| 9 | 8 | 6 | 1 | 4 | 7 | 5 | 2 | 3 |
| 1 | 6 | 8 | 2 | 7 | 4 | 3 | 5 | 9 |
| 7 | 4 | 9 | 5 | 1 | 3 | 6 | 8 | 2 |
| 2 | 3 | 5 | 8 | 6 | 9 | 4 | 1 | 7 |
| 8 | 2 | 1 | 9 | 3 | 6 | 7 | 4 | 5 |
| 3 | 5 | 7 | 4 | 8 | 1 | 2 | 9 | 6 |
| 6 | 9 | 4 | 7 | 5 | 2 | 8 | 3 | 1 |

## p.125

1. *Unforgiven*, *Braveheart*,
*Titanic*, 2. 123456, password,
12345678, qwerty, abc123,
123456789, 111111,
1234567, 3. Riga, Vilnius,
Minsk, Tallinn, Kiev, 4. *All's
Well That Ends Well*, *As You
Like It*, *A Midsummer Night's
Dream*, *Othello*, *Antony and
Cleopatra*

## p.129

1. Paris, 2. Madrid,
3. Ankara, 4. Buenos Aires,
5. Islamabad, 6. Ottawa,
7. Seoul, 8. Mogadishu,
9. Maputo, 10. Banjul,
11. Antananarivo,
12. Ouagadougou

## p.130

1. Sun lounger, 2. Passport,
3. First class, 4. Boarding
pass, 5. Face mask

## p.131

1. Mambo and mamba,
2. Coal and coax, 3. Quilt and
built, 4. Jerry and berry,
5. Foal, foul and fowl

## p.134

1. Abundant; Scarce,
2. Captivity; Freedom,
3. Bend; Straighten

## p.136

1. 828 metres (2,716 feet),
2. 50 hours, 3. 24.4 metres
(80 feet), 4. 8,095.4 metres
(about five miles!), 5. 116
metres (380 feet), 6. 122
years (she quit smoking
when she reached 117!),
7. 635 kilograms (100 stone),
8. 11 years, 130 days

## p.138

1. 40, 2. 32, 3. Three
(Oregon, Oklahoma, Ohio),
4. Five, 5. Nine, 6. 12, 7.
400, 8. 12 (it's one thousand
billion)

## p.139

| | | | |
|---|---|---|---|
| ¹B | ²A | ³T | ⁴H |
| ⁵A | R | E | A |
| ⁶L | I | A | R |
| ⁷D | A | R | E |

## p.140

Answer: Apron, napkins,
sausages, steak

## p.142

1. Last orders, 2. Pint glass,
3. Beer mat, 4. Barmaid,
5. Landlady, 6. Regular,
7. Saloon

## p.144

1. Estonia, 2. *Seven*,
3. Islam, 4. Muhammad Ali,
5. Snooker
Answer: Messi

## p.147

Answer: Bails, shin pad,
dartboard, dodgeball

## p.148

Answer: Monkey, money,
"Money, Money, Money",
ABBA, ABBA

## p.149

| 1 | 2 | 3 | 4 | 5 | 6 | 7 |
|---|---|---|---|---|---|---|
| S | K | Y | F | A | L | L |

## p.150

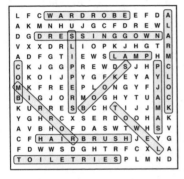

## p.155

1. Atomic Kitten, 2. Snoop Dogg, 3. The Eagles, 4. Steppenwolf, 5. Seal, 6. Lionel Richie, 7. Pussycat Dolls, 8. Def Leppard

## p.156

1. *Get Out,* 2. *Fight Club,* 3. *Kill Bill,* 4. *La La Land,* 5. *Traffic,* 6. *Bad Santa,* 7. *Raging Bull,* 8. *Scream,* 9. *Vertigo*

## p.159

1. True, 2. True, 3. False (125 caps), 4. True, 5. True, 6. False (she's Miley Cyrus's godmother), 7. False (it was horseradish), 8. True

## p.163

Answer: Beauty

## p.164

Answer: Pork pie, scone, hot dog, meatballs, sandwich

## p.166

1. Soup, prawn cocktail, (garlic) mushrooms, 2. Fake tan, deodorant, perfume, 3. "Away in a Manger", "Little Donkey", "Silent Night", 4. Trumpet, recorder, flute, 5. Yawn, get coats, tidy up

## p.168

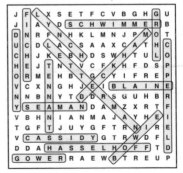

## p.171

| 1 | 2 | 3 | 4 | 5 | 6 | 7 |
|---|---|---|---|---|---|---|
| B | A | R | B | E | L | L |

## p.174
Answer: All hands on deck

## p.175
Answer: Wonderful (well, I did give you a big clue!)

## p.178
1. Ole Gunnar Solskjær,
2. Florence Griffith Joyner,
3. Gary Player, 4. Sachin Tendulkar, Sourav Ganguly, Rahul Dravid, VVS Laxman,
5. Craig Chalmers, 6. Rafael Nadal, 7. Zico, 8. Judd Trump, 9. Adrian Lewis,
10. Bret Hart

## p.179
1. Yellow, 2. Purple,
3. Green, 4. Blue, 5. Pink
Answer: Purple – it's not a snooker-ball colour

## p.180
One possible solution: DARE, CARE, CART, HART, HARP, CARP

## p.181
Answer: Croquet, table tennis, sumo wrestling, archery

## p.183
Answer: Car insurance (geddit?!)

## p.185
1. True, 2. False, 3. True,
4. False – the pawn also can,
5. True, 6. False, 7. False – it was "Jingle Bells", 8. True,
9. False, 10. True – eight times

## p.186
1. Billie Jean King,
2. Morphine, 3. Black or white
Answer: Found in titles of Michael Jackson songs

## p.188

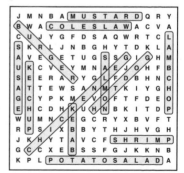

**p.190**

Answer: May the force be with you

**p.191**

| ¹S | ²T | ³U | ⁴D |
|----|----|----|----|
| ⁵P | O | S | E |
| ⁶A | G | E | S |
| ⁷M | A | R | K |

**p.192**

Answer: Goatee

**p.193**

Answer: d

**p.196**

One possible solution:
SOUR, SOAR, BOAR,
BEAR, HEAR, HEAT

**p.197**

1. Emu, 2. Wallaby, 3. Dingo,
4. Jackal, 5. Wombat
Answer: Jackal is the odd
one out. All the others are
Australian animals

**p.200**

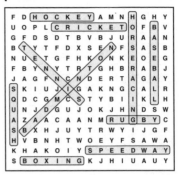

**p.203**

1. Empire State Building,
2. Honor Blackman,
3. Golden Gate Bridge,
4. *Mastermind*, 5. A cricket
stump

**p.204**

Answer: Women's rights

**p.205**

Answer: Rucksack

**p.208**

Answer: Mark Zuckerberg

**p.209**

Answer: Ashes, seamer, run
out, third umpire

| C | H | O | I | R |
|---|---|---|---|---|
| H |   | T |   | U |
| O | T | T | E | R |
| I |   | E |   | A |
| R | U | R | A | L |

Red Herring: CLUE 3

## p.217

| 8 | 6 | 4 | 3 | 2 | 5 | 7 | 1 | 9 |
|---|---|---|---|---|---|---|---|---|
| 7 | 2 | 5 | 6 | 9 | 1 | 3 | 8 | 4 |
| 3 | 1 | 9 | 7 | 8 | 4 | 5 | 2 | 6 |
| 9 | 4 | 3 | 8 | 5 | 7 | 2 | 6 | 1 |
| 2 | 8 | 7 | 9 | 1 | 6 | 4 | 5 | 3 |
| 1 | 5 | 6 | 4 | 3 | 2 | 9 | 7 | 8 |
| 4 | 7 | 1 | 5 | 6 | 9 | 8 | 3 | 2 |
| 6 | 9 | 8 | 2 | 7 | 3 | 1 | 4 | 5 |
| 5 | 3 | 2 | 1 | 4 | 8 | 6 | 9 | 7 |

## p.211
Answer: Something

## p.212
Answer: *Casablanca* (it's the address for the White House, which is what *casa blanca* means when translated into English)

## p.213
1. Green, 2. Blood, 3. Jack, 4. Table, 5. Post

## p.214
1. Willis Tower, Chicago, 2. Auckland, 3. Petronas Towers in Kuala Lumpur, 4. San Francisco, 5. Dubai

## p.216
1. Cantona, 2. Neymar, 3. Maldini, 4. Rivaldo, 5. Sampras
Answer: Sampras. The others are footballers.

## p.218
Answer: Beckham, Maradona, Agüero, Owen

## p.219
1. Hansel, 2. Sponge, 3. Berlin, 4. Drogba, 5. Godiva
Answer: Bangladesh

## p.220
1. Tequila, vodka, white rum, gin, Cointreau, lemon juice, simple syrup, cola, 2. "Please Please Me", "With the Beatles", "A Hard Day's Night", "Beatles for Sale", "Help!", "Rubber Soul", "Revolver", "Sgt Pepper's Lonely Hearts Club Band", 3. Maine, New Hampshire, Massachusetts, Rhode Island, Connecticut, New York, New Jersey, Delaware, Maryland, Virginia, North Carolina, South Carolina, Georgia, Florida

**p.222**
Answer: *Breaking Bad*

**p.223**
Answer: Quickstep, tango,
jitterbug, American smooth

**p.226**
Answer: Pygmy
hippopotamus (you were told
it was a "little" clue!)

**p.227**
1. Tiger, 2. Elephant,
3. Gorilla, 4. Jaguar,
5. Orangutan, 6. Polar bear,
7. (Giant) panda, 8. Lion,
9. Rhino, 10. Leopard
(two species)

**p.229**
Answer: *Top Gun*

**p.230**
1. b, 2. c, 3. c, 4. b

**p.233**
Answer: Rhythmic gymnastics
(a women-only event – no
dads allowed to participate!)

**p.234**
Answer: A pair of dice

# THE DAD ANNUAL

*The ultimate compendium of hilarious games, bad jokes, mind-boggling trivia and much, much more!*

**Michael Spicer**

# THE DAD ANNUAL
The Ultimate Compendium of Hilarious Games, Bad Jokes, Mind-Boggling Trivia and Much, Much More!

Michael Spicer

Format: Hardback

ISBN: 978-1-78783-298-5

Bursting with puzzles, quizzes, trivia and games, this dad-tastic annual packs in hours of fun for fathers everywhere! Whether you're keen to know where you rank on the leader board of all-time "cool dads", want to try your hand at some perplexing puzzles or you just want to add some new dad-dancing moves to your already extensive repertoire, this annual does it all!
Includes:

- Dad style guides
- Delicious "dad recipes"
- Fascinating fact files
- A compendium of conundrums to solve

… and much, much more!

# MAN STUFF

## STUFF

### A BOOK FOR BLOKES

**RAY HAMILTON**

# MAN STUFF
A Book for Blokes

Ray Hamilton

Format: Hardback

ISBN: 978-1-78685-794-1

## What makes a man?

Forget the tired old rules about what a man should or shouldn't be. Life's just too short. Being a man is meant to be fun, thrilling and fulfilling. But there's no harm in a few handy ideas to help you up your game – a style tip here, a life hack there, some adventures to boost your bucket list, even a recipe or two (for the barbecue and beyond). *Man Stuff* contains all this priceless wisdom and more, including a look at classic male hobbies like sport and technology as well as sound advice on health and fitness. Dive in and decide for yourself what kind of man you might be!

# LIFE HACKS FOR DADS

## Handy Hints to Make Life Easier

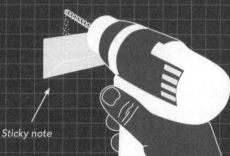

Sticky note

Cordless drill
(corded drills are
also acceptable)

Dan Marshall

Over **100** amazing hacks inside!

# LIFE HACKS FOR DADS
Handy Hints to Make Life Easier

Dan Marshall

Format: Paperback

ISBN: 978-1-84953-805-3

**Do you aspire to master the art of the perfect burger?**

**To make DIY disasters a thing of the past?**

**To discover ingenious ways to keep
the kids entertained and make cleaning
up after them a breeze?**

*Life Hacks for Dads* is your handy guide to making
your daily life that little bit easier. This fully illustrated
manual covers everything from keeping your car door
wonderfully dent-free to perfecting your Frisbee throw,
and much, much more.

Have you enjoyed this book?
If so, find us on Facebook at **Summersdale
Publishers**, on Twitter at **@Summersdale** and
on Instagram at **@summersdalebooks** and
get in touch. We'd love to hear from you!

# www.summersdale.com

## Image credits